7

D0477425

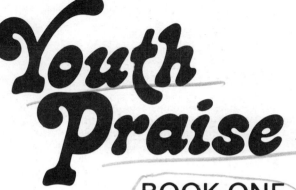

# Youth Praise

## BOOK ONE

### NUMBERS 1–150

2 vols.

*A collection of Christian hymns, songs,*
*choruses and spirituals.*

Compiled and edited by Michael Baughen
assisted by Richard Bewes

FALCON BOOKS
EASTBOURNE

ISBN 0 85491 801 9 (Boards)

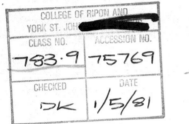
Printed in Great Britain for
FALCON BOOKS – KINGSWAY PUBLICATIONS LTD
Lottbridge Drove, Eastbourne, E. Sussex BN23 6NT by
Richard Clay (The Chaucer Press) Ltd, Bungay, Suffolk

# CONTENTS

MY LIPS SHALL GREATLY REJOICE
WHEN I SING UNTO THEE;
AND MY SOUL,
WHICH THOU HAST REDEEMED

*Psalm 71,23*

# INTRODUCTION

THIS BOOK has been compiled to try to meet the evident need for a composite youth music book in Christian youth groups of many kinds. Its purpose is not to provide 'musical entertainment with a religious flavour', but the provision of words and tunes, in adequate number and variety, to allow contemporary expression of youth praise and prayer and worship.

No one is expected to find every item in the book to his particular taste. The compiler and his helpers have drawn together choruses and songs already in use in widely different situations, and from different parts of this country. They have also added a considerable quantity of new material, and a number of translations. Tastes vary widely in the matter of Christian youth music, and the aim has been to provide a book in which all tastes will find a good selection which they can sing.

The quality of music as well as of words shows considerable variation from page to page, and this again is to serve the differing needs of those who will use the book. Some groups have pianists (and guitarists) who 'do their best' and who need simple music; others have accomplished musicians who can manage something more difficult. On the whole, it has been thought best to offer music suitable for the less able musician, in the belief that others will be able to develop their own harmonies and arrangements.

The book is a mixture of old and new, and is classified into sections so that it can be used purposefully rather than 'just for the sake of singing'. Experiments for two years before publication have shown the value of this arrangement, although any classification of chorus music must be somewhat arbitrary.

A list of acknowledgements follows, which must be read in conjunction with the acknowledgement of sources that will be found against words and music at the foot of each page. Most items in the book are copyright, and the compiler and publishers gratefully acknowledge many kindnesses in permitting the inclusion of copyright material. Every effort has been made to trace copyright-holders, but any errors or omissions will gladly be put right at the first opportunity.

# ACKNOWLEDGEMENTS

THE EARLIER STAGES of the work were in the hands of a committee which included the Revs. R. T. Bewes, M. H. Botting, M. D. Drury, J. M. Filby, C. P. Gane, K. W. Habershon, J. F. Perry, G. H. Reid, T. O. Walker, and D. C. K. Watson. We benefited greatly from the interest and encouragement of the Revs. J. R. W. Stott and T. Dudley-Smith.

The main task of the compiler since then has been greatly eased by the assiduous work of the Rev. R. T. Bewes, who has been responsible for the inclusion of most of the gospel songs and spirituals to be found in the book.

Musical arrangements have been undertaken by a number of helpers, including notably the Rev. N. L. Warren, Messrs M. C. T. Strover, G. R. Timms, D. G. Wilson, Mrs J. B. Wooldridge, and Miss P. C. Butler. Several people, including J. Roberts, have helped with the guitar chords, but the great majority of these are the work of S. G. Kitchen and A. Betts-Brown.

We are grateful to those who have given unstinted clerical help at different stages, including Mrs H. P. Brooks, Mrs R. E. Dyton, Miss E. M. Hopper, Miss P. Monk, and Miss M. A. Ogden; and we thankfully acknowledge the continual help and guidance of Mr F. W. Birkenshaw and Mr S. G. Kitchen.

My thanks go to all who have helped in so many ways, and my final, special thanks are for my wife, who has patiently borne with me, and with much hospitality for others, during the whole time of the preparation of this book.

M.A.B.

# Praise and Thanks

## 1. We will sing

*Music:* G. Brattle
*Words:* L.C. Barnes

We will sing of our Re-deem-er, He's our King:___

G  D  Em  Bm  C  Am

All His glo-ry, all His praise to you___ we bring;

Am6  Em  Am6  B7  E  A7  D

With our hearts and with our voi-ces Him we sing.___

G  D  Em  Bm  C  E7  Am

We love the Lord, we love His Word, He's our King.___

Am7 Em Am Cm6  Dm6 F Dm6 B°  A7  D  D7  G

# 2. Come and Praise

*Words:* Anon.
*Music:* Traditional
*arr.* P.C. Butler and D.G. Wilson

*Start with Chorus*

*Chorus*    Come and praise the Lord our King, Hallelujah,
Come and praise the Lord our King, Hallelujah.

1. Christ was born in Bethlehem, Hallelujah,
Son of God and Son of Man, Hallelujah:
*Chorus*

2. He grew up an earthly child, Hallelujah,
Of the world, but undefiled, Hallelujah:
*Chorus*

3. Jesus died at Calvary, Hallelujah,
Rose again triumphantly, Hallelujah:
*Chorus*

4. He will cleanse us from our sin, Hallelujah,
If we live by faith in Him, Hallelujah:
*Chorus*

5. We will live with Him one day, Hallelujah,
And for ever with Him stay, Hallelujah:
*Chorus*

# 3. Tell out, my soul!

*Words:* T. Dudley-Smith
*Music:* M.A. Baughen

**With a swing**

1. Tell out, my soul, the greatness of the Lord; Un-numbered bless-ings give my spir-it voice; Ten-der to me the promise of His Word; In God my Saviour shall my heart re-joice.

2. Tell out, my soul, the greatness of His Name!
Make known His might, the deeds His arm has done;
His mercy sure, from age to age the same;
His Holy Name — the Lord, the Mighty One.

3. Tell out, my soul, the greatness of His might!
Powers and dominions lay their glory by.
Proud hearts and stubborn wills are put to flight,
The hungry fed, the humble lifted high.

4. Tell out, my soul, the glories of His Word!
Firm is His promise, and His mercy sure.
Tell out, my soul, the greatness of the Lord
To children's children and for evermore!

# 4. There's no greater name

*Words and Music:* M.A. Baughen

**With a good swing – fairly fast**

There's no great - er Name than Je - sus,

Name of Him who came to save___ us, In that

sav - ing Name of Je - sus Ev - 'ry knee___ should

bow.___ Let ev - 'ry - thing that is 'neath the

ground, Let ev - 'ry - thing in the world a - round,

Let ev - 'ry - thing tnat's high o'er the sky Bow at

Ab        Db6     Db     Bb7

Je - sus' Name.____ In our minds by

Eb7        Ab     Fm

faith pro - fess - ing, In our hearts by

Bbm7     Eb7     Ab     Fm

in - ward bless - ing, On our tongues by words con -

Bb7     Eb7 Bb7 Eb7   Ab   C7   Fm   C°   Db6

-fess - ing, Je - sus Christ____ is Lord!____

Eb       Eb7       Ab

# 5. When morning gilds the skies

*Words:* Anon. 19th Century German
*tr.* E. Caslon
*Music:* D.G. Wilson

2. Be this, when day is past,
   Of all my thoughts the last,
   'May Jesus Christ be praised!'
   The night becomes as day,
   When from the heart we say:
   'May Jesus Christ be praised!'

3. Does sadness fill my mind,
   A solace here I find,
   'May Jesus Christ be praised!'
   When evil thoughts molest,
   With this I shield my breast:
   'May Jesus Christ be praised!'

4. To God, the Word on high,
   The hosts of angels cry,
   'May Jesus Christ be praised!'
   Let mortals, too, upraise
   Their voice in hymns of praise:
   'May Jesus Christ be praised!'

5. Let earth's wide circle round
   In joyful notes resound,
   'May Jesus Christ be praised!'
   Let earth and sea and sky,
   From depth to height, reply:
   'May Jesus Christ be praised!'

6. Be this while life is mine
   My canticle divine,
   'May Jesus Christ be praised!'
   Be this the eternal song,
   Through all the ages long:
   'May Jesus Christ be praised!'

# 6. There is joy in the presence

*Words and Music:* G.R. Timms

There is joy in the presence of the angels___ of God Ov - er

D  G  D7  G  B7  C  Am  G  Em

one sinner that re - pen - teth.___ There is joy in the presence of the

Am7  D  D7  G  D7  G  D7  G  D7  G  B7

angels___ of God Ov - er one sinner that re - pen - teth.___ For the

C  Am  G  Em  Am7  D  G

Son of Man is come to seek, To seek and to save that

Ab7  Db  Dbm6  Ab  Eb7  Ab  Fm  Ab+  Cm  Fm6

which was lost. There is joy in the presence of the angels___ of God Ov - er

B  F#7  B  D7  G  D7  G  B7  C  Am  G  Em

one sin-ner that re - pen - teth,___ Praise the Lord for His love and for His

Am7 | D | D7 | G | Gb+ | F6 | E7 | Am | E7 | Am | A7

heav-en a - bove, where His saints shall re - joice for ev - er.___

D | D7 | G | C | Am7 | D | G

# 7. I'm singing for my Lord

*Words:* J. Smith
*Music:* R. Harper

I'm sing-ing for my Lord___ ev-'ry-where I go,

C7 | F | F7 | Bb | F

Sing - ing of His wondrous love that the world may know

Bb | F | G7 | C

How He saved a | wretch like me | by His death on | Cal - var - y: I'm

F    F7    Bb

singing for my | Lord____ | ev - 'ry - where I | go. | go.

F    A7    Dm    G7    C7    F    F

2. I'm singing, but sometimes heavy is the rod,
For this world is not a friend to the grace of God;
Yet I sing the whole day long, for He fills my heart with song,
I'm singing for my Lord everywhere I go.

3. I'm singing for the lost just because I know
Jesus Christ, whose precious blood washes white as snow;
If my songs to Him can bring some lost soul I'll gladly sing:
I'm singing for my Lord everywhere I go.

4. I'm singing, for the saints as they journey home;
Soon they'll reach that happy land where they'll never roam,
And with me they'll join and sing praises to our Lord and King:
I'm singing for my Lord everywhere I go.

## 8. Sweet is the work

*Words:* I. Watts
*Music:* H. Parker

Sweet is the work, my God, my King, To praise Thy
Name, give thanks and sing, To show Thy love by
morn - ing light, And talk of all Thy truth at night.

© Joshua Duckworth Ltd, Colne, Lancs   By kind permission

## 9. We sing a loving Jesus

*Words:* S. Doodney
*Music:* N.L. Warren

1. We sing a lov - ing Jesus

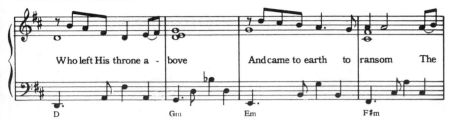

Who left His throne a - bove    And came to earth    to ransom    The

D              Gm           Em              F#m

chil - dren of His love;____    It is an oft - told story,

F         E7      A7      D                  A7

And yet we love to_ tell    How Christ, the King of glo-ry

D9        G       Gm6                 D

1-3    Once deigned with man to dwell.    4  face

A7              D              D    A7  D

2. We sing a lowly Jesus
No kingly crown He had
His heart was bowed with anguish
His face was marred and sad;
In deep humiliation
He came, His work to do
O Lord of our salvation
Let us be humble too.

3. We sing a mighty Jesus
Whose voice could raise the dead
The sightless eyes He opened
The famisl.ed soulsHe fed.
Thou camest to deliver
Mankind from sin and shame;
Redeemer and life-giver,
We praise Thy Holy Name!

4. We sing a coming Jesus
The time is drawing near
When Christ with all His angels
In glory shall appear.
Lord, save us, we entreat Thee,
In this Thy day of grace,
That we may gladly meet Thee,
And see Thee face to face.

# 10. Christ triumphant

*Words:* M. Saward
*Music:* M.A. Baughen

**With triumphant vigour**

2. Word incarnate, truth revealing,
Son of Man on earth,
Power and majesty concealing
By Your humble birth.
Yours the glory and the crown-
The high renown-
The eternal name.

3. Suffering servant, scorned, ill-treated,
Victim crucified,
Death is through the cross defeated
Sinners justified.
Yours the glory and the crown-
The high renown-
The eternal name.

4. Priestly King, enthroned for ever
High in heaven above,
Sin and death and hell shall never
Stifle hymns of love.
Yours the glory and the crown-
The high renown-
The eternal name.

5. So, our hearts and voices raising
Through the ages long,
Ceaselessly upon you gazing
This shall be our song.
Yours the glory and the crown-
The high renown-
The eternal name.

*CHRIST TRIUMPHANT* Suggested accompaniment for verses 2 & 4 arranged by D. G. Wilson.

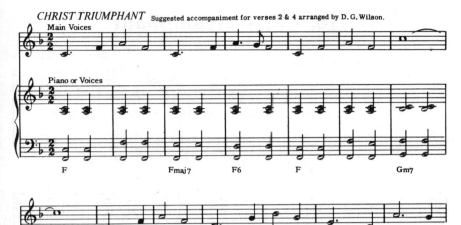

*CHRIST TRIUMPHANT* Suggested arrangement for verse 3 by H. Clifton.

**With a 2 bar swing**

# 11. Lord of the cross

*Words:* **M. Saward**
*Music:* **M.A. Baughen**

1. Lord of the cross of shame,
Set my cold heart a-flame
With love for you, my Saviour and my Master;
Who on that lonely day
Bore all my sins a-way,
And saved me from the judgement and disaster.

2. Lord of the empty tomb,
Born of a virgin's womb,
Triumphant over death, its power defeated;
How gladly now I sing
Your praise, my risen King,
And worship you, in heaven's splendour seated.

3. Lord of my life today,
Teach me to live and pray
As one who knows the joy of sins forgiven;
So may I ever be,
Now and eternally,
United with the citizens of heaven.

# 12. Jesus Christ is my Lord and King

*Words and Music:* M.A. Baughen
*arr.* P.C. Butler

*Start with chorus*

*Chorus*   Jesus Christ is my Lord and King,
To Him honour and glory bring,
Join the mighty host in heav'n above
   and praise His gracious Name.

1.   He who now is reigning in majesty
Stooped to bear our sin in humility
There on Calvary - Jesus died for me -
Died to set me free - eternally!
        *Chorus*

2.   Justified by faith we have peace with God
Fellowship with Him through our Saviour's blood,
Wonder though it be - sons of God are we -
In His family - eternally!
        *Chorus*

# 13. Thank you

**Words:** M.G. Schneider
*tr. and adapted* S. Lonsdale and M.A. Baughen
*Music:* M.G. Schneider
set out in key changes by D.G Wilson

Thank You_ for ev-'ry new good morn-ing, Thank You_ for ev-'ry fresh new day,

E    C♯m7    F♯m    B13    E    C♯m7    F♯m7    B7

Thank You_ that I may cast my burdens Wholly on to You. (Piano)

E    E7    Dm7 E7    A    Am    E    B7    E    C7

Thank You_ for ev-'ry friend I have, Lord, Thank You_ for ev-'ry-one I know,

F    Dm7    Gm    C13    F    Dm7    Gm7    C7

Recorded by Petula Clark on Pye 7N15606 in another translation by J. Fishman.
Printed choir editions (SSA and SATB) available from Bosworth & Co. Ltd

# 14. Oh, thank the Lord

*Words:* Anon
*Music:* Traditional German air

Oh, thank the Lord, oh thank the Lord, Give Him the praise for He is good; Be-cause His mer-cy does en-dure, His faith-ful-ness is ev-er sure; Oh thank the Lord, oh thank the Lord, Give Him the praise for He is good.

# 15. O Lord most high

*Music:* Old Melody
*Words:* N. J. Clayton

**Majestically**

O Lord most high, Thou ho-ly God and Sav-iour, Thy pow'r and might are more than tongue can tell, But great-er far the love that planned sal-va-tion And saved the lost from sin and death and hell.

CHORUS

O God of Love, O God of Cal-va-ry, How great Thou art! How great Thou art! In all the world there is no one like Thee, How great Thou art, How great Thou art!

2. Once far from God, an alien and a stranger,
Of hope bereft, a sinner lost and lone,
But Jesus came to rescue from the danger,
To give us life He sacrificed His own.
*Chorus:*

3. In mercy rich, in love and grace abounding,
When we were dead in trespasses and sins,
Thine only Son for us was freely given,
How great Thou art! in Thee our life begins.
*Chorus:*

# At the Beginning of a Meeting

## 16. Open Thou my eyes

*Words and Music:* G.R. Timms

# 17. Lord, you look

*Words and Music:* H. Banter
*tr.* S. Lonsdale and M.A. Baughen

Lord, You look with goodness on us,

Lord, You pour Your love up-on us,

And You prom-ise in Your Word To

hear us when we pray.

# 18. Come among us, Lord

*Words and Music:* G. Brattle

With spirit

Come a - mong us, Lord, Gath - ered round Thy Word, To mind and heart Thy truth im - part, O liv - ing Word. In this {morn - ing / ev - 'ning} hour, Lord, re - veal Thy power! May souls be fed with liv - ing bread: Come a - mong us Lord!

# 19. By blue Galilee

*Words and Music:* E.H. Swinstead

By blue Ga - li - lee Je - sus walked of old,

By blue Ga - li - lee wondrous things He told.

Sav - iour, still my teacher be, Showing won - drous things to me,

As of old by Ga - li - lee, Blue Ga - li - lee.

## 20. Turn your eyes

*Words and Music:* H.H. Lemmel

Turn your eyes up-on Je - sus, Look full in His won-der-ful face;____ And the things of earth will grow strange-ly dim In the light of His glo-ry and grace.____

## 21. Break Thou the bread of Life

*Words:* M.A. Lathbury
*Music:* W.F. Sherwin

Break Thou the Bread of Life, dear Lord, to me, As Thou didst

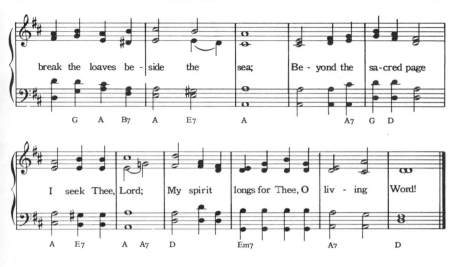

break the loaves be-side the sea; Be-yond the sa-cred page I seek Thee, Lord; My spirit longs for Thee, O liv-ing Word!

## 22. Speak to us, Lord

*Words and Music:* **G. Brattle**

Speak to us, Lord, in this brief hour to-day; Give light up-on the written word we pray; Stir heart and mind to heed and to__ o-bey, For this we plead.

© G. Brattle By kind permission

# 23. Triumphant victor

*Words and Music:* G. Brattle

# God's Love and Grace

## 24. God's love is wonderful

*Words and Music:* S.E. Cox

God's love is wonder-ful, God's love is wonder-ful,— Wonderful that He should give His Son to die for me, God's love is wonderful.

## 25. On Calvary's tree

*Words:* A.W. Edsor
*Music (melody):* A.E. Walton
*arr.* A.W. Edsor

On Calv'ry's tree He died for me, That I His love might know.—

To set me free He died for me, That's why I love Him so.

# 26. Wonderful grace of Jesus

*Words and Music:* H. Lillenas

*Guitar players accompanying this hymn may prefer key D as indicated by chord symbols in brackets.

## 27. Higher than the hills

*Words and Music:* N. J. Clayton

Higher than the hills, Deeper than the sea, Broader than the skies above is my Redeemer's love for me; To His cross of shame, Jesus freely came, Bearing all my sin and sorrow Wondrous love!

## 28. In the garden Gethsemane

*Words and Music:* J. Jurgens
*tr. and adapted* S. Lonsdale and M.A. Baughen

**Moderato**

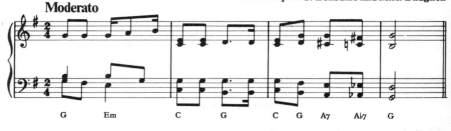

2. In the garden Gethsemane
   Christ Jesus knelt alone,
   Yet where were His disciples when
   He faced the cross alone?
   Eyes were heavy, sleep was easy,
   They let Him watch alone
   In the garden Gethsemane:
   Christ Jesus knelt alone.

3. In the garden Gethsemane
   Christ Jesus knelt alone,
   "Father" He said, "Thy will be done"
   Christ Jesus knelt alone;
   Then the cross for our salvation
   For us then to atone:
   In the garden Gethsemane
   Christ Jesus knelt alone.

4. In the garden Gethsemane
   Christ Jesus knelt alone,
   And now today He looks to us
   To those He calls His own;
   Are we watching? Are we praying?
   Or are we failing Him?
   In the garden Gethsemane
   Christ Jesus knelt alone.

## 29. The grace of the Lord

*Words:* J.S. Holden
*Music:* C.H.M. Foster

The grace of the Lord, like a fath-om-less sea Suf-fi-cient for you, suf-fi-cient for me, Is ten-der and patient and bound-less and free Suf-fi-cient for ev-'ry need.

## 30. Living, He loved me

*Words:* J.W. Chapman
*Music:* C.H. Marsh

Liv-ing, He loved me; dy-ing, He saved me; Bur-ied, He

*Guitar players accompanying this hymn may prefer key D as indicated by chord symbols in brackets.

car - ried my sins far a - way;____ Ris- ing, He jus - ti - fied
free - ly for ev - er; One day He's com - ing — O glo - ri - ous day!____

## 31. For God so loved the world

*Words:* F. Townsend
*Music:* A.B. Smith

For God so lov'd the world, He gave His on - ly Son, To

die on Calvary's tree, From sin to set me free; Some day He's coming

back, What glo - ry that will be, Won - der - ful His love to me.

# 32. Two thousand years

*Words:* A. Boddington and R.T. Bewes
*Music:* R.T. Bewes
*arr.* M.C.T. Strover

1. It was just two thousand years a - go He walked thro' Ga - li -
lee, The e - ter - nal God had stepped be - low In human form to
be; Born of a low - ly He - brew maid, A car - pen - ter He
gives me peace and pur - pose true, A power that's old but

*Fine*

was by trade; He came down, Two thou-sand years a - go:
ev - er new; God came down, Two thou-sand years a - go.

E7  D  A9  D  G9(add6)  D

They tell of Je-sus' glo-ry, Who met Him in the way; And it

G  G6  D  D9(add6)  A9  A7  D6

*D.S. al Fine*

- is no id-le sto-ry, for He lives in me to-day: He

G6  D  E7  A7  *D.S. al Fine*

2.  It was just two thousand years ago
    He died on Calvary;
    It was for sin He suffered so,
    Though innocent was He.
    My sin and guilt lay on His head;
    My penalty He bore instead;
    He suffered,
    Two thousand years ago.

        *Chorus*

3.  It was just two thousand years ago
    An empty tomb was found;
    The stone was rolled away we know,
    The powers of hell are bound;
    My risen Lord is now on high,
    He lives that we may never die,
    He triumphed!
    Two thousand years ago:

        *Chorus*

## 33. Oh, the love that drew

*Words:* W.R. Newell
*Music:* D.B. Turner

Oh, the love that drew sal - va - tion's plan! Oh, the grace that brought it
down to man! Oh, the might - y gulf that God did span at Cal - va - ry!
Mer - cy there was great, and grace was free; Par - don there was mul - ti -
plied to me; There my burdened soul found li - ber - ty, at Cal - va - ry.

## 34. Just because

*Words and Music:* A.E. Kelly

1. Just be-cause He set His heart on me, Just be-cause His pow'r could

set me free, Just because of my in - i - qui-ty

C     G7 C        Am        E7        F        F#°

**V.1** Je - sus died. **V.2** Je - sus rose. **V.3** Je - sus reigns.

C   G+   C      C   G+   C      C   G9   C

2.  When by Him the ransom was supplied,
    When by Him the debt was satisfied,
    When by Him we could be justified
        Jesus rose.

3.  Now of Calvary each Christian sings,
    Now with praise to Christ all heaven rings,
    Now He's Lord of Lords and King of Kings
        Jesus reigns.

© A.E. Kelly  By kind permission

## 35. His compassions fail not

*Words and Music:* G.R. Timms

His com-pas - sions fail___ not, fail___ not, ___

C     Em7    F    G    C    G7    C    Dm7    G7

His com-pas-sions fail___ not,_ They are new ev - 'ry morning.___

C  Em7  D9  Em  Am  E+  C6  C°  Dm7 Am6  Dm  G7  C

Great is Thy faithfulness, Great is Thy faithfulness;

Dm7      Am  G7  C      Am  E7  Am  D7  G7

His com-pas -sions fail___ not,_ They are new ev - 'ry day.

F   Em Fmaj7 G7  Am  C7  F    C  C°  G7  C

© G.R. Timms 1964 By kind permission

# 36. Can it be true?

*Words and Music:* Brother William
*arr.* The Venturers

Can it be true, the things they say of You?

You walked this earth shar-ingwith friends You knew

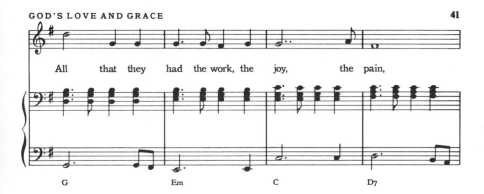

All      that   they   had   the work, the      joy,          the   pain,

G              Em              C              D7

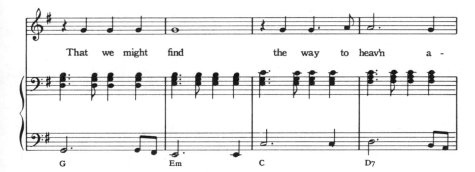

That    we    might    find          the    way    to    heav'n     a -

G              Em              C              D7

D.S.   | Last time

- gain.

G              Em              C              D7            G

D.S.

2.   And day by day You still return this way;
     But we recall there was a debt to pay:
     Out of Your love for Your own world above,
     You left that holy thing, Your endless love to prove.

3.   Can it be true, the things they did to You-
     The death, the shame, and were Your friends so few?
     Yet You returned again alive and free-
     Can it be true, my Lord, it had to be.

# 37. I know a fount

*Words and Music:* O. Cooke

I know a fount where sins are wash'd a - way, (a - way);

E   F#7   B   B7   E        B7   E   F#m   E   B7   E

I know a place where night is turned to day (to day);

E        D#   D#7   G#m   C#7   B        F#7        B   B7

Bur - dens are lift - ed, blind eyes made to see:— There's a

E   B7   E        B7   C#m        F#m   F#9   B7        E

won - der work - ing pow'r in the blood of Cal - va - ry.

B   E   B   B7        E        E7        A   E   B7        E

# 38. Tell me, Lord Jesus

*Words and Music:* M. Snowdon

*mf* 1. Tell me Lord Je - sus; Why did You have to

Dm        F   Gm   F        Bb        Gm

die,— Mas - ter? Tell me Lord Je - sus:— Why did You have to

die? And You die? came down to earth from

heaven will - ing - ly, There at Cal - var - y, On the curs - ed tree,

There You died for me. There You died for me. D.C.

2. Pride, sin and wrong in us,
   That cut us off from God, our Father,
   When we were bound in sin,
   That's when You came to die.

   And You came down to earth,
   From heaven willingly,
   There at Calvary,
   On the cursed tree,
   There You died for me,
   There You died for me.

3. You came to set us free,
   That's why You had to die, Master,
   To give us liberty,
   That's why You had to die.

# 39. New every morning

*Words and Music:* M.A. Baughen
*arr.* W. Wooldridge

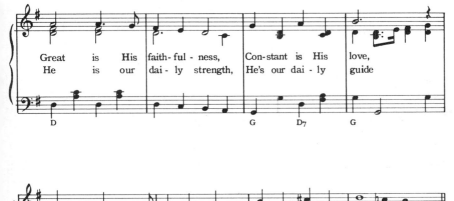

Great is His faith-ful-ness, Con-stant is His love,
He is our dai-ly strength, He's our dai-ly guide

D                  G   D7   G

Great is His sav-ing pow'r Coming from a - bove!
If we will wait on Him And in Him a - bide!

D   A7     D        G   A7   D7

*D.C.*

## ⊕ CODA

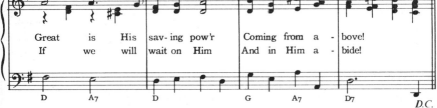

New!\_\_\_\_\_ ev - 'ry morning it's new!\_\_\_\_\_ The mer - cy

G6             G7   C6             Cm

of the Lord is won-der-ful - ly new!

G        D7        G

# 40. Jesu, lover of my soul

*Words* C. Wesley
*Music:* D.G. Wilson

2. Other refuge have I none;
Hangs my helpless soul on Thee;
Leave,ah, leave me not alone;
Still support and comfort me.
All my trust on Thee is stayed;
All my help from Thee I bring;
Cover my defenceless head
With the shadow of Thy wing.

3. Thou, O Christ, art all I want;
More than all in Thee I find;
Raise the fallen, cheer the faint,
Heal the sick and lead the blind.
Just and holy is Thy Name,
I am all unrighteousness;
False and full of sin I am,
Thou art full of truth and grace.

4. Plenteous grace with Thee is found,
Grace to cover all my sin;
Let the healing streams abound;
Make and keep me pure within.
Thou of life the fountain art,
Freely let me take of Thee;
Spring Thou up within my heart,
Rise to all eternity.

# 41. Ride on, ride on in majesty!

*Words:* H.H. Milman
*Music:* D.G. Wilson

2. Ride on, ride on in majesty!
In lowly pomp ride on to die;
O Christ, Thy triumphs now begin
O'er captive death and conquered sin.

3. Ride on, ride on in majesty!
The angel armies of the sky
Look down with sad and wondering eyes
To see the approaching sacrifice.

4. Ride on, ride on in majesty!
Thy last, Thy fiercest strife is nigh;
The Father on His sapphire throne
Awaits His own anointed Son.

5. Ride on, ride on in majesty!
In lowly pomp ride on to die;
Bow Thy meek head to mortal pain,
Then take, O God, Thy power, and reign.

# *Testimony*

## 42. Jesus died for me

*Words and Music:* G.R. Timms

Je-sus died for me,____ His blood has made me free.

Now He lives with-in me and He leads the way;

While I trust in Him____ I've vic-t'ry ov-er sin:

Praise His Name He loves me so, And He shall be my King.

# 43. There is a Name

*Words:* F. Whitfield
*Music:* W.H. Rudd

1. There is a Name I love to hear, I love to speak its worth;—— It sounds like mu-sic in my ear, The sweet-est Name on earth:——

**CHORUS**

Oh, how I love the Sa-viour's Name, Oh, how I love the Sa-viour's Name,
(Altos) How I love the Sa-viour's Name, How I love the Sa-viour's Name, How I

Oh how I love the Sa-viour's Name, The sweet-est Name on earth: (on earth):
love I love the Sa viour's Name,

2. It tells me of a Saviour's love,
   Who died to set me free;
   It tells me of His precious blood,
   The sinner's perfect plea:
   *Chorus*

3. It tells of one whose loving heart
   Can feel my deepest woe,
   Who in my sorrow bears a part
   That none can bear below:
   *Chorus*

4. It bids my trembling heart rejoice,
   It dries each rising tear;
   It tells me in a 'still, small voice'
   To trust and never fear:
   *Chorus*

5. Jesus, the Name I love so well,
   The Name I love to hear!
   No saint on earth its worth can tell,
   No heart conceive how dear!
   *Chorus*

# 44. Christ for me

*Words and Music:* A. Burns

Christ for me,— yes, it's Christ for me,

[1] He's my Saviour, my Lord and King; I'm so hap-py I shout and sing;

[2] Ev - 'ry day as I go my way it is Christ for me.—

# 45. 'Tis marvellous and wonderful

*Words and Music:* C.H. Morris

1. The Saviour has come in His might - y pow'r, And spo - ken

peace to my soul,— And all of my life from that ve - ry hour I've

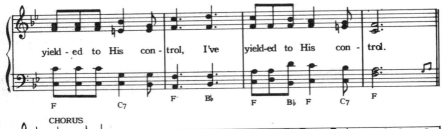

yield - ed to His con - trol, I've yield-ed to His con - trol.

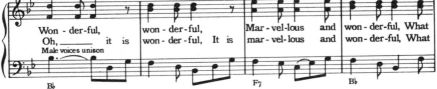

CHORUS

Won - der - ful, won - der - ful, Mar - vel-lous and won - der-ful, What
Oh, _____ it is won - der-ful, It is mar - vel-lous and won - der-ful, What

Male voices unison

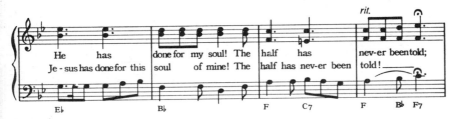

He has done for my soul! The half has nev-er been told;
Je - sus has done for this soul of mine! The half has nev-er been told!

rit.

a tempo

Oh _____ { It is won - der - ful, It is mar - vel - lous and won - der - ful,
won - der - ful }

What Je-sus has done for this soul of mine! The half has never been told!

rit.

2. From glory to glory He leads me on,
From grace to grace ev'ry day,
And brighter and brighter the glory dawns
While pressing my homeward way,
While pressing my homeward way.

*Chorus*

3. If fellowship here with my Lord can be
So inexpressibly sweet,
O what will it be when His face we see,
When round the white throne we meet,
When round the white throne we meet?

*Chorus*

# 46. Life is wonderful now

*Words and Music:* I. Sutherland

1. There's a psalm of praise fill - ing all my days, Since to Jesus my heart did bow;

O what melody! Glorious harmony! Life is wonderful now:____

**CHORUS**

Life is wonderful, Yes, it's wonderful! Life is wonderful now to me!

I let Jesus in, He changed ev-'ry-thing, Life is wonderful now!

Since His blessings came in - to my heart, Joy un-speak-a-ble fills ev-'ry part,

And I want to live for my Lord;___ Life is won-der-ful now!

B♭   F7  B♭  Cm   F7   B♭ F7  B♭

2. All is happiness, gone is my distress,
   Peace and vict'ry He does endow;
   Since my Saviour came, I can't be the same;
   Life is wonderful now:
   *Chorus*

3. All my life is praise for His wondrous grace,
   I will serve the Lord, this my vow;
   Jesus came to me, and He set me free;
   Life is wonderful now:
   *Chorus*

© I. Sutherland 1957 and 1958 By kind permission

# 47. Jesus came from Heaven

*Words and Music:* G.R. Timms

Je - sus came from hea — ven With a humble birth,

D♭   D♭°   G♭6   B♭7

Took man's form up - on Him To live with us on earth.

G♭   Fm A♭7(add6)  B♭m  E♭7  A♭

Je - sus grew to man - hood In God's per-fect plan,

D♭   D♭°   G♭6   B♭

Told us of His Fa - ther And His great love for man.

Je - sus died at Cal - v'ry To wash my sins a - way,

Now He reigns in glo - ry on high.

Je - sus lives with - in me All a - long life's way,

Je - sus came from hea - ven for me!

© G.R. Timms 1964 By kind permission

# 48. In my need Jesus found me

*Words and Music:* G. Brattle

# 49. Gone! Gone!

*Words and Music:* H. Griggs

Gone! Gone! Gone! Gone! Yes, my sins are gone. Now my soul is free and in my heart's a song. Bur-ied in the deepest sea. Yes, that's good enough for me. I shall live e-ter-nal-ly. Praise God! my sins are gone.

# 50. I'm not ashamed

*Words and Music:* G.R. Timms

I'm not a - shamed not a - shamed of the gos - pel of

Christ    For it  is  the  pow'r of  God    un- to— sal -

E      E7      A    D    A    E7    A      D    Bm

-va - tion  To——  ev - 'ry- one  to——  ev - 'ry- one that be - liev — eth

A    E  C♯7      F♯m Bm7  E  E      A  E7  F♯m  Bm    E  E7  A

## 51. Joined to the vine

*Words and Music:* R. McCurdy Jones

Joined  to  the  vine  as  a  branch of  the  tree,

G              B7              C6  C        G

Cleansed by His  word that  He's  spoken  to  me,  Stemmed in His  love  as  He

D7              G    C  G          B7

wants me  to  be:  Bear - ing  the  fruit  of  the  Lord,—

C6    C  Cm6    G  B7  Dm6  A9    D7  G

# 52. He lives!

*Words and Music:* A.H. Ackley

He lives!___ He lives!___ Christ Je-sus lives to-day!___ He

walks with me and talks with me A-long life's nar-row way.___ He

lives!___ He lives,___ Sal-va-tion to im-part!___ You

ask me how I know He lives— He lives with-in my heart.___

# 53. Thou shalt guide me with Thy counsel

*Words and Music:* G.R. Timms

Thou shalt guide me with Thy coun-sel___ And af-ter

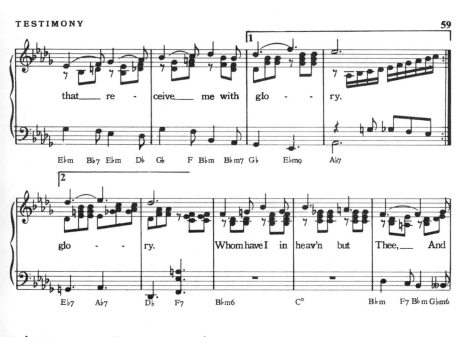

that___ re - ceive___ me with glo - ry.

Ebm   Bb7   Ebm   Db   Gb   F   Bbm   Bbm7   Gb   Ebm9   Ab7

glo - - ry.   Whom have I in heav'n but Thee,___ And

Eb7   Ab7   Db   F7   Bbm6   C°   Bbm   F7   Bbm   Gbm6

who on earth more dear to me?___

Db   Dbm6   Eb7   Gbm6   Ab7   Eb7   Ab7

Thou shalt guide me with Thy coun - sel___ And af - ter

Db   Eb   Eb°   Db   Abm   Bb7   Ebm   Bb7

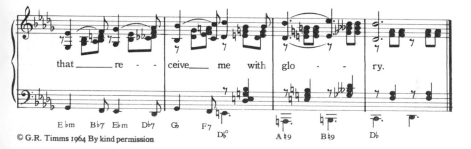

that___ re - ceive___ me with glo - - ry.

Ebm   Bb7   Ebm   Db7   Gb   F7   Db°   Ab9   Bb9   Db

# 54. Now I belong to Jesus

*Words and Music:* N. J. Clayton

1. Je-sus my Lord will love me for ev-er, From Him no pow'r of e-vil can
se-ver He gave His life to ran-som my soul, Now I be-long to Him:

**CHORUS**

Now I be-long to Je - sus, Je-sus be-longs to me,
Not for the years of time a - lone, But for e-ter-ni-ty.

2. Once I was lost in sin's degradation,
Jesus came down to bring me salvation.
Lifted me up from sorrow and shame,
Now I belong to Him:

*Chorus*

3. Joy floods my soul for Jesus has saved me,
Freed me from sin that long had enslaved me,
His precious blood He gave to redeem,
Now I belong to Him:

*Chorus*

© N. J. Clayton 1943 By kind permission

# 55. All that thrills

*Words and Music:* T. Harris

1. Who can cheer the heart like Je - sus, By His presence

all di - vine? True and ten-der, pure and pre - cious,

O how blest to call Him mine!

REFRAIN

All that thrills my soul is Je - sus; He is more than life to me, (to me), And the fair-est of ten thou - sand In my bless-ed Lord I see.

2. Love of Christ so freely given,
Grace of God beyond degree,
Mercy higher than the heaven,
Deeper than the deepest sea:
*Chorus*

3. What a wonderful redemption!
Never can a mortal know
How my sin, tho'red like crimson,
Can be whiter than the snow:
*Chorus*

4. Ev'ry need His hand supplying,
Ev'ry good in Him I see;
On His strength divine relying,
He is all in all to me:
*Chorus*

5. By the crystal flowing river
With the ransom'd I will sing,
And for ever and for ever
Praise and glorify the King:
*Chorus*

# 56. Things are different now

*Words and Music:* S.W. Gavitt

Things are diff'rent now, something happened to me When I gave my heart to

Je - sus. Things are dif - f'rent now; I was chang'd, it must be, When I
*(unison D.S.) Things are dif - f'rent now: something happened that day When I*

gave my heart to Him.___
*gave my heart to Him.___*

*Unison*
Things I loved be - fore have

passed a - way, Things I love far more have come to stay.

## 57. It's an open secret

*Words and Music:* J. Webb

It's an o - pen se - cret, I love my Sa - viour so._____

know; Se - cret, O I love Him so.

Em    G    D7    G

And you can seek Him, find Him, Share this se - cret,

C    G    G°

too; Know His lov - ing kind - ness in ev - 'ry - thing you

G    Em    Bm    Em    A7

# 58. No one ever cared for me like Jesus

*Words and music:* C. F. Weigle

oth - er friend so kind as He; No one

else could take the sin and dark - ness from me

O how much He cared for me.

2. All my life was full of sin when Jesus found me,
All my heart was full of misery and woe;
Jesus placed His strong and loving arms about me,
And He led me in the way I ought to go:
*Chorus*

3. Ev'ry day He comes to me with new assurance,
More and more I understand His words of love;
But I'll never know just why He came to save me
Till some day I see His blessed face above:
*Chorus*

# 59. He gives me satisfying peace

*Words and Music:* N. J. Clayton

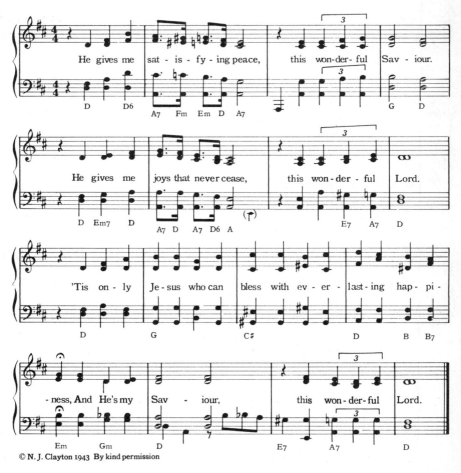

He gives me sat-is-fy-ing peace, this won-der-ful Sav-iour.
He gives me joys that never cease, this won-der-ful Lord.
'Tis on-ly Je-sus who can bless with ev-er-last-ing hap-pi-ness, And He's my Sav-iour, this won-der-ful Lord.

© N. J. Clayton 1943 By kind permission

# 60. Jesus is a wonderful Saviour

Traditional
*arr.* W.G. Hathaway

Je-sus is a won-der-ful Sav-iour, He will carry you thro',

Je - sus is a won-der-ful Sav - iour, He will car-ry you thro', my bro-ther;

Je - sus is a won-der-ful Sav - iour He will car-ry you thro', And when the

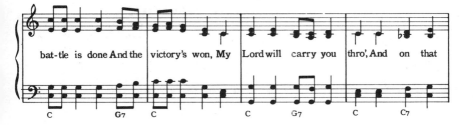

bat-tle is done And the victory's won, My Lord will carry you thro', And on that

last day____ When you're fac-ing your Mak - er,____ You'll need my

Je - sus____ To be your Sav - iour;____ He'll ev - er

hide you___ in the rock of a - ges,___ The rock of

F  C  G7  C

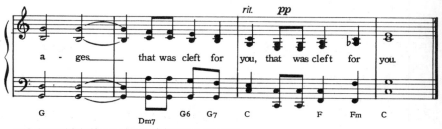

*rit.*  **pp**

a - ges___ that was cleft for you, that was cleft for you.

G  Dm7  G6  G7  C  F  Fm  C

© Music copyright in this arrangement only by Victory Press Ltd.
By kind permission

## 61. Jesus is the Saviour

*Words and Music:* M. Wood
*arr.* G.R. Timms

Je - sus is the Saviour whom I love to know,

G  Dm7

Bass an octave lower and well marked.

Heaven is the haven that I'm going to___  Je - sus is the captain who now

G  G+  C

leads my life; Un - wor - thy as I am I know He came to save A

sin - ner such as me, a sin - ner such as me He came to save from the

*Fine* CHORUS

grave: For God so loved the world that He gave His

on - ly be - gotten Son That who - so - ever be -

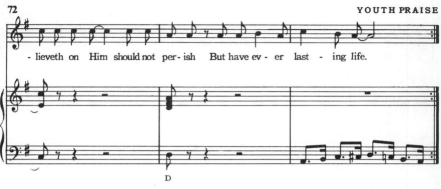

- lieveth on Him should not per-ish But have ev-er last-ing life.

2. Sometimes when you're feeling all alone and blue,
Jesus can come in and help to pull you through;
Sometimes you just know that you need Jesus too,
So come on sinner, come to Him, He died for you
A sinner such as you, a sinner such as me
He came to save from the grave:

*Chorus*

3. Jesus is the Saviour whom I love to know,
Heaven is the haven where I'm going to go;
Jesus is the captain who now leads my life,
Unworthy as I am I know He came to save
A sinner such as me, a sinner such as me
He came to save from the grave:

# 62. Walking in the King's highway

*Words:* B.D. Ackley
*Music:* A.H. Ackley

Days are filled with glad-ness, nights are filled with song,_ Walking in the King's high-

-way (High-way___) And the world grows brighter, as we pass a long,_

King's high-way I'm walking)

Walking in the King's high-way. Walking, walk-ing in the King's high-way,
(Yes I'm)

A    A7    D    C°    A7    C°    A7

Walking in the King's high-way, To the place of man-y mansions
(The King's highway)

A7    D

I shall come at last,___ Walking in the King's high-way.

Em    A7    D

2. Music from the homeland fills me with delight,
   Walking in the King's highway;
   Visions of the glory break upon my sight,
   Walking in the King's highway.
   *Chorus*

3. Crowned with tender mercies, guarded by His love,
   Walking in the King's highway;
   Jesus gives a foretaste of the joys above,
   Walking in the King's highway.
   *Chorus*

# 63. The King of Love

*Words:* Sir H.W. Baker
*Music:* The Followers
*arr.* D.G. Wilson

ev - - er.

Fm7    Bb7        Eb          B    C#    Eb

2. Where streams of living water flow
   My ransomed soul He leadeth,
   And where the verdant pastures grow
   With food celestial feedeth.

4. In death's dark vale I fear no ill
   With Thee, dear Lord, beside me;
   Thy rod and staff my comfort still,
   Thy cross before to guide me.

3. Perverse and foolish oft I strayed,
   But yet in love He sought me
   And on His shoulder gently laid
   And home, rejoicing, brought me.

5. Thou spread'st a table in my sight;
   Thy unction grace bestoweth;
   And O, what transport of delight
   From Thy pure chalice floweth!

6. And so through all the length of days
   Thy goodness faileth never;
   Good Shepherd, may I sing Thy praise
   Within Thy house for ever.

# God's Invitation

## 64. Rise up and walk

*Words and Music:* G.R. Timms

Rise up and walk! All pow'r is giv-en un-to Him, He

chan-ges not, and sin shall not have vic-t'ry ov-er you.

Rise up and walk! He is the Lord that heal-eth thee, At

His command thou shalt be free, Christ Je-sus makes you whole!

# 65. There is full salvation

*Words:* **M.A. Baughen**
*Music:* **N.L. Warren**

2.  He gives fellowship and guidance all the way:
    As we pray— ev'ry day;
    He gives fellowship and guidance all the way:
    There is no friend like Jesus.

3.  Death is swallowed up for all eternity:
    Death will be— victory!
    Death is swallowed up for all eternity:
    We trust a risen Jesus.

4.  There is full salvation through that precious Name:
    Jesus came— took our blame;
    There is full salvation through that precious Name:
    No other name like Jesus.

# 66. Ho! everyone

YOUTH PRAISE

*Words and Music:* **M.A. Baughen**

Ho! ev-'ryone that thirsts in life Hear the off - er of the Lord;

He is the one who sat - is - fies— Come of_ your own ac-cord.

Let the wick-ed for -sake his way And the un- righteous his thoughts;

Let him return to the Lord our God And he will find pardon and mer - cy— a-

- bundant-ly! Seek ye the Lord while He may be found, Call on Him while He's

near; Find Him as Saviour Lord and King Know Him by love instead of fear.

# 67. Behold I stand

*Words and Music:* C. Blissard-Barnes

Behold I stand, I stand at the door and knock, Behold I stand at the door and knock; If any man will hear my voice Let him open the door and I will come in and sup with him and he with me.

# 68. Behold I stand

*Words and Music:* **M.A. Baughen**

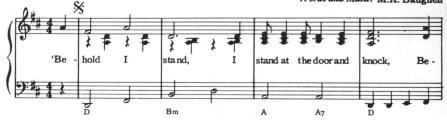

'Be - hold I stand, I stand at the door and knock, Be -

- hold I stand, I stand at the door and knock; If

an - y man will lis - ten to my voice, and

*rit last time*

op - en that door_____ I will come in.'

*Fine.*

This is the in - vi - ta - tion that Je - sus gives to you, This

is the promise of His Word and it is true. When

F♯    Bm    Bm7    E7    A7    D.S.

When He comes in it's fellowship divine,
For I am His and He is mine;
When He comes in, then He will sup with me
Until that day His face I'll see.

This is the invitation that Jesus gives to you,
This is the promise of His Word and it is true.

Behold He stands, He stands at the door and knocks,
Behold He stands, He stands at the door and knocks;
If any man will listen to His voice, and open that door—
He will come in.

© M.A. Baughen 1964 By kind permission

## 69. There's a way back to God

*Words and Music:* E.H. Swinstead

There's a way back to God from the dark paths of sin; There's a

D7    G    G°    G    D    D7    G    F♯    F♯7    D7

door that is o-pen and you may go in: At Cal-va-ry's cross is

G    Em    Bm    Em    Am    A9    D    D7    G    G°    G

where you be-gin, When you come as a sin-ner to Je — sus.

G    Dm    G7    C    G°    G    C    G    D7    G

# 70. I heard the voice of Jesus

*Words:* H. Bonar
*Music:* N.L. Warren

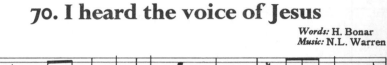

I heard the voice of Je - sus say, 'Come un-to me and

F    Dm    Gm    C7    F    B♭

rest, Lay down thou weary one, lay down Thy head up-on my

F    Am    Dm    Gm    C7    F    Dm    G7

**Brighter**

breast.' I came to Je - sus as I was,

A    C7    F    Dm    Gm7    C7

Wear - y and worn and sad, I found in Him a

Dm    G7    C6    C7    F    Dm

**1 & 2**

rest - ing place And He has He has made me

Gm7    Am    D7    Gm7    C    G9    C7

F    B♭    F    C₇    C    G₉  C₇  F  F⁶

2.   I heard the voice of Jesus say,
'Behold, I freely give
The living water: thirsty one,
Stoop down and drink, and live.'
I came to Jesus and I drank
Of that life-giving stream;
My thirst was quenched, my soul revived,
And now I live in Him.

3.   I heard the voice of Jesus say,
'I am this dark world's light,
Look unto me, thy morn shall rise,
And all thy days be bright.'
I looked to Jesus and I found
In Him my star, my sun;
And in that light of life I'll walk,
Till travelling days are done.

## 71. Get on the road

*Words:* M.A. Baughen
*Music:* N.L. Warren

*(To be sung to the tune of No. 70)*

1.   Broad is the way that leads man to
The place that's called destruction;
Narrow the way to life anew,
The way which few will walk on:

*Chorus*   Get on the road which leads you to God
Start at the cross of Jesus;
He is the way, the truth, and the life-
So trust Him, come and follow Jesus (Jesus).

2.   God has prepared a place for all
Who trust in Christ as Saviour;
His promise is that at His call
We'll live with Him for ever:
    *Chorus*

3.   We can draw near to God in prayer,
Know Him as Friend and Father;
We can approach God without fear,
And know His love forever:
    *Chorus*

4.   No other way to God is true,
No other way than Jesus,
No other way to God for you-
Jesus alone can save us:
    *Chorus*

# 72. If you want joy

*Words and Music: arr.* W.G. Hathaway

If you want joy, real joy, won-der-ful joy, let Jesus come in-to your heart. If you want joy, real joy, won-der-ful joy, let Je-sus come in to your heart.___ Your sins He'll take a-way,___ your night He'll turn to day___ Your heart He'll make o-ver a-new, and then come in to stay. If you want joy, real

joy, won-der-ful joy, let Je-sus come in-to your heart.

Dm  Gm  C7  F  Gm  F  C7 F C7  F

# 73. Jesus is knocking

*Words and Music:* G. Brattle

Je-sus is knock-ing, pa-tient-ly wait-ing, Out-side your

F  Dm  Gm  C  Dm  Dm7

heart's closed door.___ Do not re-ject Him, sim-ply ac-

G9  G7  C  C7  F  Dm  Gm

-cept Him, Now and for-ev-er-more.___

A9  A7  Gm7  F  C7  F

# 74. In Christ there is full salvation

*Words and Music:* A.E. Kelly

# Challenge

## 75. Take up the cross

*Words:* R. J. B Eddison
*Music:* G.E.F. Rawlins

"Take up the cross, thyself deny, Come boldly after Me." The Saviour calls: let us reply, "Lord, I will follow Thee." "Take up the cross, deny yourself, Come boldly after Me." The Saviour calls: Lord give us grace to rise and follow Thee.

# 76. Make up your mind

*Words and Music:* R.T. Bewes
*arr.* M.C.T. Strover

Which way are you choosing, the nar-row or broad? You'll have to make up your mind.\_\_\_\_ Just give up your own way and fol-low the Lord; Why don't you make up your mind?\_\_\_\_ He died, the strang-er of Ga-li-lee, to bring sal-va-tion to you and me; A strong com-pan-ion you'll prove Him to be, So won't you make up your mind?\_\_\_

2. Which crowd will you follow, the large or the small?
Be sure to make up your mind.
The cost is demanding, but hear Jesus call;
Then come and make up your mind.
Your friends may shun you unthinkingly,
But Christ gives power and liberty;
To life with purpose you'll find the key,
When once you make up your mind!

3. On which are you resting, the Rock or the sand?
You'd better make up your mind!
With Christ as foundation your building will stand,
But have you made up your mind?
Temptations and trials must come your way,
The storms of Judgement will rage one day;
Take Jesus and on Him your confidence stay,
Don't wait, but make up your mind!

4. O what will you do with the Saviour today?
He bids you make up your mind.
Repent and accept Him without delay,
O sinner, make up your mind!
Why stumble alone along the road?
He'll sort your tangles, He'll take your load,
And in your heart He will make his abode;
It's time to make up your mind!

© R.T. Bewes 1964   By kind permission

# 77. You'd better get on that road

*Words and Music:* M.C. Dunlop

O there's on-ly one way to heaven, bro-ther, And you'd bet-ter get on that road, For it leads from Cal-va-ry's rug-ged cross to the

gates of the ci - ty of God. For oth - er roads will

E    B7    E    A

lead a - stray, So take the strait and nar - row way; And you'd

E    F#m    B    E    F#7    B    B7

bet-ter get on that road, You'd bet-ter get on that road.

E    B    E    A    E    B7    E

2.    O there's only one way to heaven, brother,
      And you'd better get on that road;
      For salvation's free, not by works you see,
      It is the gift of God's love bestowed.
      Your sin on Christ was fully laid,
      Its penalty is really paid;
      So you'd better get on that road,
      You'd better get on that road.

3.    O there's only one way to heaven, brother,
      And you'd better get on that road;
      For Christ is the door, and His word is the key
      To a home in that blest abode.
      He is the Truth, the Life, the Way,
      O trust Him now without delay;
      And you'd better get on that road;
      You'd better get on that road.

# 78. How long

*Words and Music:* M. Wood
*arr.* G.R. Timms

How long, how long be-fore you

come to the Sav-iour?___ Oh sin-ner, tell me how long.___

___ You know, yes you know you're lost, And

so to the Sav-iour___ you certain-ly must go.___

___ Well, Jesus died on Cal-vary To save the lost like

you and me; But still you go on living that way: Come on now, come

G    D    G    B

.under His sway. So come a - long, you'll sing that new

E7    A    A7    D

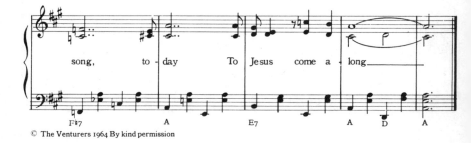

song, to - day To Jesus come a - long_____

F♯7    A    E7    A    D    A

## 79. Christian are you running

Words: H.V. Davies
Music: D.G. Wilson

**With a bounce (♩=c.90)**

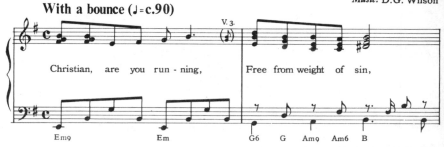

Christian, are you run - ning, Free from weight of sin,

Em9    Em    G6    G    Am9    Am6    B

With the hope be-fore you A crown of life to win?

Em9    A   B   Em    C9 (maj 7)   G   G6   Am7

Or is your bur-den heav-y, Each step like backward pace:

D7   G     C    C6    Bm

How are you pro-gress - ing In the Christian race?

1-3     D. C. 4

Am Dm G9   C9 (maj7)   Am      D7    G

2. Where as you are running
Do you fix your eyes,
Are they set on Jesus
With faith that never dies?
Or is your vision dazzled
With idols on the way:
How are you progressing
In the race today?

3. Are you ever mindful
Of watchers yet unseen,
Saints of God before you
Who in the race have been?
Or are your thoughts still dwelling
On things the world holds dear:
How are you progressing—
Keep the vision clear.

4. Christian, press thou onwards,
Looking to the Lord,
Think now how His life-blood
Was for thy soul outpoured;
Then leave all burdens with Him,
O never drag that load,
End the race rejoicing,
In that blest abode.

# 80. The Jericho road

*Words and Music:* D.S. McCrossan
*arr.* L.G. Presley

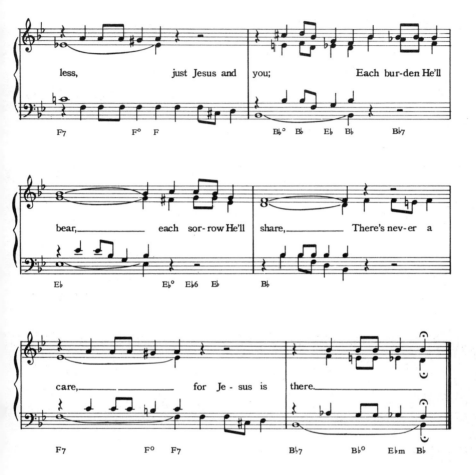

2. On the Jericho road blind Bartimaeus sat,
   His life was a void, so empty and flat;
   But Jesus appeared, one word brought him sight,
   On the Jericho road, Christ banished his night.

3. O brother, to you this message I bring,
   Though hope may be gone, He'll cause you to sing;
   At Jesus' command sin's shackles must fall,
   On the Jericho road, will you answer His call?

# 81. If any man will follow

*Words and Music:* **M.A. Baughen**

**With vigour**

If an - y man will fol - low, if an - y man will fol - low,
Let him de - ny himself, oh, let him take up his cross, And

If any man will fol - low af - ter my Je - - sus:
let him come and fol - low af - ter my

Lord!___ Who - so - ev - er will live for self will throw his life a -
Who - so - ev - er will be ashamed of Je - sus and His

- way, Christ gives life to all who fol - low Him
words, In this sin - ful age in which we live,

What is a man ad - van - taged if he gains the whole wide
Je - sus the King will be ashamed of him in that great

**To ✠ Coda** (last time)

world | And then | los - es | his | soul!___
day | When in | glo - ry | He | comes!___

F Dm7 G7 C7 D.C.

Last time only

Let him | come and | fol - low | af - ter my | Lord!___

Dm F G9 Bbm7 Abm Dm7 Cm7 C7 F

1. If any man will follow, if any man will follow,
   If any man will follow after my Jesus:
   Let him deny himself, oh, let him take up his cross,
   And let him come and follow after my Lord!

   Whosoever will live for self will throw his life away,
   Christ gives life to all who follow Him—
   What is a man advantaged if he gains the whole wide world
   And then loses his soul!

2. If any man will follow, if any man will follow,
   If any man will follow after my Jesus:
   Let him deny himself, oh, let him take up his cross,
   And let him come and follow after my Lord!

   Whosoever will be ashamed of Jesus and His words,
   In this sinful age in which we live,
   Jesus the King will be ashamed of him in that great day,
   When in glory He comes!

3. If any man will follow, if any man will follow,
   If any man will follow after my Jesus,
   Let him deny himself, oh, let him take up his cross,
   And let him come and follow after my Lord!
   Let Him come and follow after my Lord

## 82. I'm glad I'm a Christian

*Words:* verses 1 & 2 Anon.
verses 3 & 4 A. Boddington
*Music: arr.* G.R. Timms

I'm glad I'm a Christ - ian,____ I'm trust-ing the Lord;____ ____ I rest on God's prom - ise____ Be-lieving His Word.

2. The past is forgiven,
And now I am free;
A mansion in heaven
Is waiting for me.

3. O come to Jesus,
Your sins all confess;
He's longing to clothe you
In His righteousness.

4. Admit you're a sinner,
Believe He is true;
And when you have found Him
Your life He'll renew.

© Music copyright in this arrangement by G.R. Timms      By kind permission

## 83. They are watching you

*Words:* R.T. Bewes
*Music:* R.T. Bewes
*arr.* M.C.T. Strover

1. Though the world has for - sa - ken God, Treads a diff -'rent path, lives a

diff-'rent way, I walk the road that the Sav-iour trod, And all may

CHORUS

know I live un-der Je-sus' sway: They are watch-ing you,_ mark-ing

all you do, Hear-ing the things_ you say; Let them

see the Saviour as He shines in you, Let His pow'r con-trol you ev-'ry day.

2. Men will look at the life I lead,
   See the side I take, and the things I love;
   They judge my Lord by my every deed—
   Lord, set my affections on things above:
   *Chorus*

3. When assailed in temptation's hour,
   By besetting sins, by the fear of man,
   Then I can know Jesus' mighty power,
   And become like Him in His perfect plan:
   *Chorus*

4. Here on earth people walk in night;
   With no lamp to guide, they are dead in sin;
   I know the Lord Who can give them light,
   I live, yet not I, but Christ within:
   *Chorus*

# 84. If you will follow Jesus

*Words and Music:* J.B. Hindley
*arr.* W. Wooldridge

If you will fol-low Je-sus You'll real-ly find a - bun-dant life, If

D7   Em7   D6

you will fol - low the Saviour; You'll real-ly find a - bun-dant life If

E   A   D   Em7   D6

you will fol - low the Lord.   If you will fol-low Je-sus Step

E7   A7   D   Bb7   Eb

out in faith up - on the way, And come and fol-low the Sa-viour; Step

Ab   Fm7   Eb   Fm   Bb   Eb

out in faith up - on the way, And come and fol-low the Lord.

Fm7   C7   Fm7   Bb7   Eb

# 85. God cares for you

*Words and Music:* M. Wood
*arr.* G.R. Timms

There's a time when you tra - vel way back in time;

When you try, to un - rav - el, and up - wards climb:

\_\_ and make my life be new.

2. The place your search leads you to has no escape;
   Up a hill to a cross it's true— a grim landscape:
   Calvary's the place you're in,
   Christ is dying for your sin,
   And you know that God cares for you. . .

3. Come with me up to His side and see His face;
   Kneel awhile, forget your pride and see His grace:
   Hear Him say "Forgive them all",
   Now listen to His call,
   And you'll find that God cares for you. . .

4. It is hard for you to understand, but try you must;
   As a child takes his father's hand you must have trust:
   Trust in Christ— He died for you,—
   Believe in this- you know it's true,
   That God cares for you . . .

# Prayer and the Bible

## 86. Never doubt the Word

*Words and Music:* R. McCurdy Jones

Not one pre - cious prom - ise of His Word Ev - er failed the ser - vants of the Lord, Tried and proved by many like fine gold, Sweeter than the hon - ey - comb:

CHORUS

Nev - er doubt the Word, God's own prec - ious Word, Nev - er doubt the Word of God. There's a

prom-ise true In the Book for you, Nev-er doubt the Word of God.

2. Ev'ryone who takes God at His Word
   Need by doubters never be deterred,
   He will find the promise, read or heard,
   Never failing to be true:
       *Chorus:*

3. Ev'ry promise can be yours or mine
   As to Him our minds in prayer incline,
   If our hearts have known His love divine
   We will want to love Him more:
       *Chorus:*

# 87. All Scriptures

*Words and Music:* M.A. Baughen
*arr.* W. Wooldridge

All Scriptures are given by the breath of God, Are in-spired of God, Are the Word of the Lord; All Scriptures are given by the breath of God, And

glor-i-fy His Name! They can make you wise to a

sav - ing faith In Je - sus Christ the Lord; They can

C    Am7   Fm    C    Gm    C

make the man of God com-plete, And are meant to be his sword!

C7   F    E7    Am   F    C    Cm   F   G7   C7    *D.C.*

1. All Scriptures are given by the breath of God,
       Are inspired of God,
       Are the Word of the Lord;
   All Scriptures are given by the breath of God,
   And glorify His Name!

   They can make you wise to a saving faith
   In Jesus Christ the Lord;
   They can make the man of God complete,
   And are meant to be His sword!

2. So study to show yourself approved to God,
       Fit to use His Word,
       Fit to speak in His Name;
   So study to show yourself approved to God,
       A workman not ashamed.

   They'll reprove, correct, and a training in
   All righteous living afford;
   They will yield up all that we need to know
   Of the teaching of the Lord!

3. All Scriptures are given by the breath of God,
       Are inspired of God,
       Are the Word of the Lord;
   All Scriptures are given by the breath of God,
   And glorify His Name!

## 88. Before you start the day

*Words:* M.A. Baughen
*Music:* R. McCurdy Jones

Be- fore you | start the day___ Take time a - | lone    to    pray, And feed up-

- on God's Word    To | know His way;___ So start the | day with Him,___Then walk the

way with Him___ and come to | eve ning time   with | praise    to    Him___

© M.A. Baughen and R. McCurdy Jones 1964 By kind permission

## 89. Lord who left the highest heaven

*Words:* T. Dudley-Smith
*Music:* M.A. Baughen

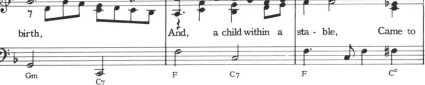

1. Lord,    who left the highest | heav - en        | For        a homeless human

birth,        | And,    a child within a | sta - ble,      Came to

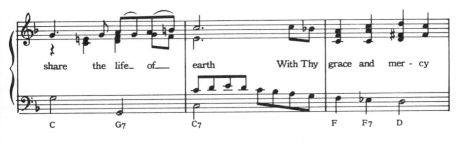

share    the life_ of__ earth    With Thy | grace and   mer - cy

C          G7          C7                        F     F7    D

bless                All who  suf - fer   home - less__ - ness

Gm                                    C7              F

2. Lord, who sought by cloak of darkness
   Refuge under foreign skies
   From the swords of Herod's soldiers,
   Ravaged homes, and parents' cries—
   May Thy grace and mercy rest
   On the homeless and oppressed.

3. Lord, who lived secure and settled,
   Safe within the Father's plan,
   And in wisdom, stature, favour
   Growing up from boy to man—
   May Thy grace and mercy bless
   Us with growth in holiness.

4. Lord, who leaving home and kindred,
   Followed still as duty led,
   Sky the roof and earth the pillow
   For the Prince of Glory's head—
   With Thy grace and mercy bless
   Sacrifice for righteousness

5. Lord, who in Thy Cross and Passion
   Helpless hung 'twixt earth and sky,
   Yet whose thoughts were for Thy mother,
   And a thief condemned to die—
   May Thy grace and mercy rest
   On the helpless and distressed.

6. Lord, who rose to life triumphant
   With man's whole salvation won,
   Risen, glorified, ascended,
   All Thy Father's purpose done—
   May Thy grace, all conflict past,
   Bring Thy children home at last.

# 90. All your anxiety

*Words and Music:* E.H. Joy

All your anx - i - e - ty, all your care, Bring to the mer - cy - seat, leave it there.

Ne - ver a bur - den He can - not bear, Ne - ver a friend like Je - sus.

# 91. O Lord, teach me to pray

*Words and Music:* Pfarrer Julius
*tr.* S. Lonsdale and M.A. Baughen

♩ = 100

O Lord, teach me to pray,

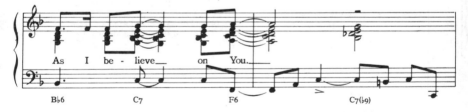

As I be - lieve on You.

O Lord, teach me to pray,

# 92. God answers prayer

*Words:* F. Wallingford
*Music:* D.M. Allen

# Strength in the Lord

## 93. Trust in the Lord

*Words and Music:* R. McCurdy Jones

Trust in the Lord, and do not be dis-cour-aged, Trust in the

Lord,___ and stop that feeling blue,___ Trust in the Lord and you will be en-

cour-aged,___ For Je-sus cares for you.___

2. Trust in the Lord, and not in any fable,
   Trust in the Lord, and find Him wholly true,
   Trust in the Lord, and know that He is able
   To fill your whole life through.

3. Trust in the Lord, and not in men or nation,
   Trust in the Lord, as Saviour, Lord, and King,
   Trust in the Lord for full and free salvation,
   And lift your heart and sing.

4. Trust in the Lord, faith is a great adventure,
   Trust in the Lord, and never cease to pray,
   Trust in the Lord, for all the unknown future,
   Today and every day!

# 94. God's will for you

*Words and Music:* M.G. Schneider
*tr. and adapted* S. Lonsdale and M.A. Baughen

2. God's will for you is good,
Ev'ry morning anew
Think upon His great faithfulness:
Sing Him your song.

3. God's will for you is good,
Stop to ponder again
All the blessings and gifts He gives:
Sing Him your song.

4. God's will for you is good,
Even sorrow and pain
Can bring blessing through His grace:
Sing Him your song.

5. God's will for you is good,
For He sent His own Son
To bear all our guilt and sin:
Sing Him your song.

6. God's will for you is good,
Be it sorrow or joy
He is faithful in life and death:
Sing Him your song.

# 95. I can do all things

*Words and Music:* M.A. Baughen

**With a swing - fairly fast**

1. I can do all things through Christ the Lord who strengthens me;
I can do all things Through Je-sus Christ my King.— For
He is the strength of my heart and my soul, O Je-sus, my Sav-i-our; And
He is my friend and my Lord and my all, O Je-sus, my Lord.

2. I can do all things
   Through Christ my Lord who strengthens me;
   I can do all things
   Through Jesus Christ my King.
   I'm kept by the pow'r of His sheltering hand,
   O Jesus, my Saviour;
   He'll bring me at last to that heavenly land
   O Jesus, my Lord.

3. I can do all things
   Through Christ my Lord who strengthens me;
   I can do all things
   Through Jesus Christ, my King!

# 96. When the road is rough

*Words and Music:* N. J. Clayton

When the road is rough and steep, Fix your eyes up-on Je - sus,

C  Am  Em  F  C6  G7  C  G+

He a - lone has pow'r to keep, Fix your eyes up-on Him;

C  Am  Em  F  C6  G7  C

Je - sus is a gracious friend, One on whom you can de - pend,

E7  A7  D7  G  G+

He is faith - ful to the end, Fix your eyes up-on Him.

C  Am  Em  F  C6  G7  C

© N. J. Clayton By kind permission

# 97. Christ be my leader

*Words:* T. Dudley-Smith
*Music:* M.A. Baughen
*arr.* C. Roberts

1. Christ be my lead - er___ By night as by day;___

Bb  Eb  Bb  F7

Safe through the dark - ness,___ For He is the Way.___

B♭

V.3
___ Nor darkness nor

___ Fears for the fu - ture___ I trust to His care;___

E° B♭ B♭7 E♭

V.3
Can touch my Sal-

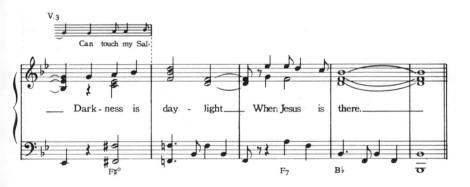

___ Dark - ness is day - light___ When Jesus is there.___

F♯° F7 B♭

2.  Christ be my teacher
    In age as in youth,
    Drifting or doubting,
    For He is the Truth.
    Grant me to trust Him;
    Though shifting as sand,
    Doubt cannot daunt me:
    In Jesus I stand.

3.  Christ be my saviour
    In calm as in strife;
    Death cannot hold me
    For He is the life.
    Nor darkness nor doubting,
    Nor sin and it's stain,
    Can touch my Salvation:
    With Jesus I reign.

# 98. When Jesus comes to you

*Words and Music:* J. Webb

(add melody, if desired)

peace; 1. The glo-ry of His pres-ence, From care will bring re-
light; 2. The glow of in-ward cour-age Will tinge the dark-est

-lease When Je-sus, Je-sus comes to you.
night,

CHORUS
melody

When Je-sus comes to you, When Je-sus comes to

# 99. Christ is the answer

*Words and Music:* T.W. Maltby

# 100. When I have sorrow

*Words and Music:* H.H. Lemmel

# 101. Just a closer walk

Traditional
*arr.* M.C.T. Strover

★ These more simple chords can be used when accompaniment is by guitar only.

*Chorus:* Just a closer walk with Thee,
Grant it, Jesus, this my plea,
Daily walking close with Thee,
Let it be, dear Lord, let it be.

2. Through this world of toils and snares,
If I falter, Lord, who cares?
Who with me my burden shares?
None but Thee, dear Lord, none but Thee:

*Chorus*

3. When my feeble life is o'er,
Time for me will be no more,
Guide me gently, safely home,
To Thy Kingdom's shore, to Thy shore:

*Chorus*

# 102. I know who holds the future

*Words and Music:* A.B. Smith and E. Clark

1. I do not know what lies a - head, The way I can - not see; Yet one stands near to be my guide, He'll show the way to me:

CHORUS

I know who holds the fu - ture, And He'll guide me with His hand, With God things don't just hap - pen, Ev - 'ry - thing by Him is planned; So as I face to - mor - row With its prob - lems large and small, I'll

trust the God of | mir - a - cles, | Give to | Him my | all.

C      E♭7    G   G7   E7      G°   Em   A7    D7      G

2. I do not know how many days
   Of life are mine to spend;
   But one who knows and cares for me
   Will keep me to the end:
       *Chorus:*

3. I do not know the course ahead,
   What joys and griefs are there;
   But one is near who fully knows,
   I'll trust His loving care:
       *Chorus:*

# 103. We'll understand it better by and by

Traditional
*arr.* M.C.T. Strover

hear the sto - ry how we've ov - er - come, And we'll

G          B   C          G          Em

VERSE

un - der - stand it better by and by. Trials dark on ev - 'ry hand, and we

*Fine*

Am9        D9              G   C   G              G7

can - not un - der - stand All the ways that God will lead us To that

C          G          D7    G    B       Em          Em7

blessed promised land, But He'll guide us with His eye And we'll

A7                      G          G7

follow till we die, And we'll un - der - stand it better by and by:

C6          Em          A7          D9          G          *D. C.*

2. Temptations, hidden snares, often take us unawares
   And our hearts are made to bleed
   For each thoughtless word and deed;
   And we wonder why the test
   When we've tried to do our best,
   But we'll understand it better by and by:
   *Chorus:*

# 104. Burdens are lifted at Calvary

*Words and Music:* J.M. Moore

1. Days are filled with sorrow and care, Hearts are lonely and drear; Burdens are lif-ted at Cal-va-ry, Je-sus is ve-ry near. *(ve-ry near)*

CHORUS

Burdens are lif-ted at Cal-va-ry, Cal-va-ry,____ Cal-va-ry;____ Burdens are lif-ted at Cal-va-ry, Je-sus is ve-ry near.____ *(ve-ry near.)*

2.  Cast your care on Jesus today,
    Leave your worry and care;
    Burdens are lifted at Calvary,
    Jesus is very near:

    *Chorus*

3.  Troubled soul, the Saviour can see,
    Ev'ry heartache and tear;
    Burdens are lifted at Calvary,
    Jesus is very near:

    *Chorus*

# Dedication

## 105. Only to be

*Words and Music:* N. J. Clayton

On-ly to be what He wants me to be, Ev-'ry mo-ment of ev-'ry day;

Yielded completely to Je-sus a-lone, Ev'ry step of this pil-grim way;

Just to be clay in the pot-ter's hands, Ready to do what His word commands,

On-ly to be what He wants me to be, Ev-'ry mo-ment of ev-'ry day.

# 106. Cleanse me

*Words and Music:* R. Hudson Pope

Cleanse me from my sin, Lord, Put Thy pow'r with-in, Lord, Take me as I am, Lord, And make me all Thine own;___ Keep me day by day, Lord, Underneath Thy sway, Lord, Make my heart Thy palace and Thy roy-al throne.

# 107. Day by day

*Words:* Richard of Chichester
*Music:* D. Austin

Day by day, dear Lord, of Thee three things I pray: To see Thee more clear-ly, To love Thee more

dear - ly,    To   fol - low   Thee more   near - ly   day   by   day.

C    C7    F    Bb6    F    C7    F

## 108. Spirit of the living God

*Words and Music: arr.* W.G. Hathaway

**Slowly with expression**

Spi - rit of the   Liv - ing God,   Fall   afresh   on   me!   Spi - rit of the

F         C    F    Bb    F    C    F

Liv - ing God,   Fall   afresh   on   me!   Break me,   melt me,   mould me,

C    F    Bb    Gm    F    C7    F    Bb    F    G    G7

fill   me!   Spi - rit of the   Liv - ing God,   Fall   afresh   on   me!

C    C7    F    C    F    Bb    F    C7    F

## 109. I'll be a friend to Jesus

*Words:* J. Oatman
*Music:* J.W. Dennis
*arr.* G.R. Timms

1. They tried my   Lord   and   Master,___ With no one   to   de -
*(my Lord)*

Eb    Bb    Eb    Bb    Eb    Cm Bb    Eb    F7

-fend;____ With-in the halls *(the halls)* of Pi-late____ He stood with-

B♭7    E♭    Fm    G    Cm7

**CHORUS**

-out a friend:____ I'll be a friend *(a friend)* to

Cm7    F7    B♭7    E♭    A♭  B♭7    E♭

Je-sus,____ My life for Him *(for Him)* I'll spend____ I'll be a

A♭    E♭    Cm    B♭    E♭    F    B♭    E♭  F9    G

friend *(be a friend)* to Je-sus,____ Until my years *(my years)* shall end.____

E♭6  B♭ A♭ E♭    Cm A♭ A♭6  E♭    B♭    E♭

2.  The world may turn against Him,
    I'll love Him to the end;
    And while on earth I'm living,
    My Lord shall have a friend:
        *Chorus:*

3.  I'll do what He may bid me,
    I'll go where He may send;
    I'll try each flying moment
    To prove that I'm His friend:
        *Chorus:*

4.  To all who need a saviour,
    My friend I recommend;
    Because He brought salvation
    Is why I am His friend:
        *Chorus:*

# 110. Bring forth the fruit

*Words and Music:* M.A. Baughen
*arr.* W. Wooldridge

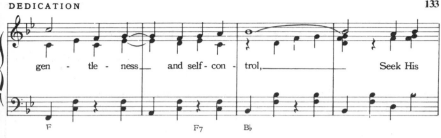

gen - tle - ness___ and self - con - trol,_____ Seek His

F       F7    B♭

good - ness_____ and His faith - ful - ness,___ And seek

F       F7     D7     Gm    B♭  B♭m

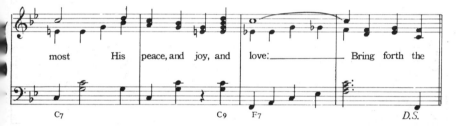

most His peace, and joy, and love:_____ Bring forth the

C7                    C9   F7                         *D.S.*

*Start with chorus*

*Chorus*    Bring forth the fruit of the Spirit in your life,
                Let the life of Christ be seen in you;
                Bring forth the fruit of the Spirit in your life,
                And let the Lord be glorified in you.

1.    Seek His patience and His kindness,
       Seek His gentleness and self-control,
       Seek His goodness and His faithfulness,
       And seek most His peace, and joy, and love:

*Chorus*    Bring forth the fruit of the Spirit in your life,
                Let the life of Christ be seen in you;
                Bring forth the fruit of the Spirit in your life,
                And let the Lord be glorified in you.

# 111. As You cleanse me

*Words and Music:* O.G. Blarr
*tr.* S. Lonsdale and adapted by M.A. Baughen

I be-gin a - new, Lord. - new, Lord.

C+ Dm C7 F6 C7 F B♭m

I be-gin a - new, Lord.

F C+ Dm Gm7 G♭7 F6

2. As You've set me in this place
And sufficient is Your grace,
As You've set me in this place
I begin anew, Lord.

3. As You're watching over me
I can face the enemy,
As You're watching over me
I begin anew, Lord.

4. As I'm ever in Your sight
In the depth or in the height,
As I'm ever in Your sight
I begin anew, Lord.

# 112. O Holy Spirit, giver of life

*Words:* M. Saward
*Music:* P.C. Butler

O Ho - ly Spi - rit giv - er of life,

E♭ Cm Fm7 B♭7

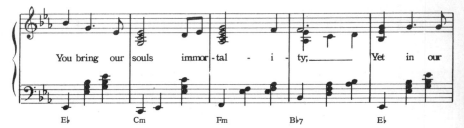

You bring our souls immor-tal - i - ty;____ Yet in our

Eb　　Cm　　　Fm　　　Bb7　　Eb

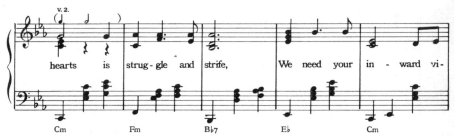

v. 2.

hearts is strug-gle and strife, We need your in - ward vi-

Cm　　Fm　　　Bb7　　　Eb　　　Cm

tal - i - ty; Work out with in us the Fath-er's de-

Ab　Bb7　Eb　Bb7　　　Eb　　　Ab　Ab6

- sign,____ Give to us life, O Spirit Di - vine.

Cm　Abm　Eb　　Gm　Cm　Fm7　Abm6　Eb　　Bb7(add6)　Eb

2.　O Holy Spirit, giver of light,
　　To minds where all is obscurity;
　　Exchange for blindness, spiritual sight,
　　That we may grow to maturity;
　　Work out within us the Father's design,
　　Give to us light, O Spirit Divine.

3.　O Holy Spirit, giver of love,
　　And joy, and peace, and fidelity;
　　The fruitfulness which comes from above,
　　That self-control and humility;
　　Work out within us the Father's design,
　　Give to us love, O Spirit Divine.

© M. Saward and P.C. Butler 1964 By kind permission

# 113. There is a place of quiet rest

*Words and Music:* C.B. McAfee

2. There is a place of comfort sweet,
   Near to the heart of God,
   A place where we our Saviour meet,
   Near to the heart of God.

   *Chorus:*

3. There is a place of full release,
   Near to the heart of God,
   A place where all is joy and peace,
   Near to the heart of God:

   *Chorus:*

# 114. According to the working

*Words and Music:* W. Wooldridge

need. So that hence-forth we might live on-ly

C C7m F F7 Bb C6

un - to Him, Our_ friend and Lord in - deed.

F F7 Bb Gm7 F C7 F
Bb7

## 115. Lord, make me useful

*Words and Music:* E.H.G. Sargent

Lord, make me use - ful to Thee,_

F Gm D7 Gm C7

Send now Thy Spir - it to me,_ Thy per - fect will

Gm7 C7 F Bb F

In me ful - fil, Lord, make me use - ful to Thee.

Gm C7 D7+9 Gm7+9 F Gm C7 F

## 116. His hands were pierced

*Words and Music:* D. Wood

2. His feet were pierced, the feet that trod
   The furthest shining star of God;
   And left their imprint deep and clear
   On ev'ry winding pathway here.

3. His heart was pierced, the heart that burned
   To comfort ev'ry heart that yearned;
   And from it came a cleansing flood,
   The river of redeeming blood.

4. His hands and feet and heart, all three
   Were pierced for me on Calvary;
   And here and now, to Him I bring,
   My hands, feet, heart, an offering.

## 117. I'll live for Jesus

*Words and Music:* P. J. Schultz

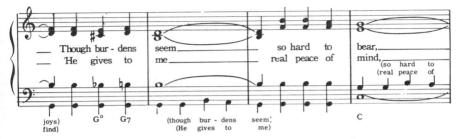

Though bur-dens seem____ so hard to bear,____
He gives to me____ real peace of mind,
(so hard to
(real peace of

joys) G° G7 (though bur-dens seem) C
find) (He gives to me)

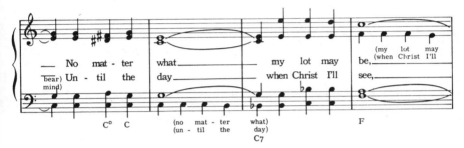

____ No mat-ter what____ my lot may be,
(my lot may
(when Christ I'll
bear) Un-til the day____ when Christ I'll see,
mind)

C° C (no mat-ter what) F
(un-til the day)
C7

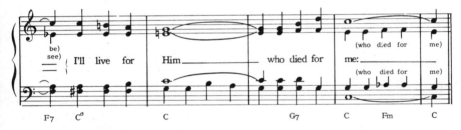

be)
see) I'll live for Him____ who died for me:____
(who died for me)
I'll live for Him
(who died for me)

F7 C° C G7 C Fm C

**CHORUS**

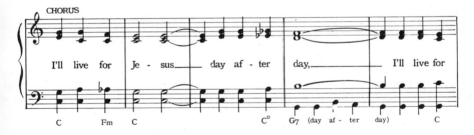

I'll live for Je-sus____ day af-ter day,____ I'll live for

C Fm C C° G7 (day af-ter day) C

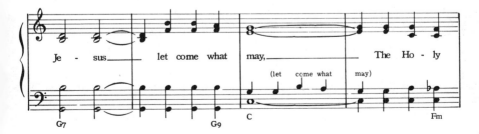

Je-sus____ let come what may,____ The Ho-ly
(let come what may)

G7 G9 C Fm

Spir - it___ I will o - bey, (I will o - bey) And live for -

*C    C7    F    F7    C    B7*

Je - sus___ day af - ter day. (day af - ter day)
                                    (day af - ter day)

*C    G7    C    F    C*

# 118. Creator God

*Words:* Anon (Indian origin)
*Music:* N.L. Warren

1. Cre - a - tor God, Cre - a - tor God! With Thee
2. Cre - a - tor God, Cre - a - tor God! With Thy
3. And with Thy heart, Cre - a - tor God, I will

*G    Em    C    D7    G    Em*

### Brighter

I am a man, But with - out Thee. O
hands may I work, With Thy feet may I
learn and love, With Thy heart, O Cre -

*Am    G    D7    G    C*

Lord my Sav-iour, With out Thee I am just a child.
walk, O Sav-iour, And through Thine own eyes let me see.
a - tor God, I'll learn and love like Thee.

*Am    D7    G    Am7    D7    G*

# 119. I'll live for Christ

*Words:* M.A. Baughen
*Music:* R. McCurdy Jones

I'll live for Christ who gave Him-self on the tree I'm cru-ci-

-fied with Christ whose death set me free, And yet I live, for Christ is

liv-ing in me: I'll live for Christ al - way, I'll live for

Christ al - way, I'll serve Him ev - 'ry day; I'll live by

faith in Christ and trust in His grace I'll live for Christ al - way.

# 120. Sing Hosanna

*Words:* (version 1) A. Sevison
(others)
*Music: arr.* The Csehys

Give me oil in my lamp, keep me burn-ing, Give me

A7   D   D7   G   A7

oil in my lamp, I pray; Give me oil in my lamp, keep me

D   E♭   E9   A7   D   D7

burn-ing, Keep me burn-ing 'til the break of day:

G   D   A7   D

2 PART CHORUS ★

Sing Ho-san-na! Sing Ho-san-na! Sing Ho-sanna to the King of Kings!

D   D7   G   E7   A7   D   G   D

Sing Ho-san-na! Sing Ho-san-na! Sing Ho-sanna to the King

D   D7   G   E7   A7   D

★ One group sustain 'Sing' while the other group does 'Sing Hosanna' etc.

*Version 2*

1. Give me joy in my heart, keep me praising,
   Give me joy in my heart, I pray;
   Give me joy in my heart, keep me praising,
   Keep me praising 'til the break of day:
   > *Chorus as version I*

2. Give me peace in my heart, keep me resting . . .
   > *Chorus*

3. Give me love in my heart, keep me serving . . .
   > *Chorus*

*Version 3*

1. What a wonderful Saviour is Jesus,
   What a wonderful friend is He,
   For He left all the glory of heaven,
   Came to earth to die on Calvary:
   > *Chorus as version I*

2. He arose from the grave, Hallelujah,
   And He lives never more to die,
   At the Father's right hand interceding
   He will hear and heed our faintest cry:
   > *Chorus*

3. He is coming some day to receive us,
   We'll be caught up to heaven above,
   What a joy it will be to behold Him,
   Sing forever of His grace and love:
   > *Chorus*

# 121. I want to walk

*Words:* St Paul's Erith 1964 Swiss Houseparty
*Music:* Swiss folk tune *(Es Buurebuebli)*
*arr.* C. Simmonds

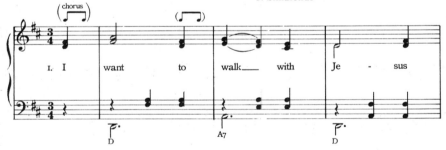

1. I want to walk⸺ with Je - sus

Christ, All the days I live of this life on earth,

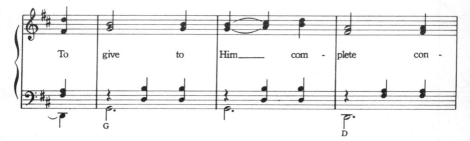

To give to Him ___ com - plete con -

trol Of bo - dy and ___ of soul: ___

1. I want to walk with Jesus Christ,
   All the days I live of this life on earth,
   To give to Him complete control
   Of body and of soul:

*Chorus*   Follow Him, follow Him, yield your life to Him,
   He has conquered death, He is King of Kings,
   Accept the joy which He gives to those
   Who yield their lives to Him.

2. I want to learn to speak to Him,
   To pray to Him, confess my sin,
   To open my life and let Him in,
   For joy will then be mine:
           *Chorus*

3. I want to learn to speak of Him,
   My life must show that He lives in me,
   My deeds, my thoughts, my words must speak
   All of His love for me:
           *Chorus*

4. I want to learn to read His Word,
   For this is how I know the way
   To live my life as pleases Him,
   In holiness and joy:
           *Chorus*

5. O Holy Spirit of the Lord,
   Enter now into this heart of mine,
   Take full control of my selfish will
   And make me wholly Thine:
           *Chorus*

# 122. He'll understand and say "Well done"

*Words:* L.E. Campbell
*Music:* pop. *arr.* B. Gilbert
*arr.* G.R. Timms

1. O when you come to the end of life's journey, Wear-y and

worn, and the battle is done, Carr-ying the Cross, the

Cross of re-demption, He'll un-der-stand and say 'Well

done', He'll un-der-stand and say 'Well done'.

2. Give, when you give, the best of your service,
   Telling the world that the Saviour has come;
   Be not dismayed if men won't defend you,
   He'll understand and say "Well done",
   He'll understand and say "Well done".

3. O when you try, and fail in your trying,
   Hands sore and scarred from the work you have begun,
   Come to the cross, come quickly to Jesus,
   He'll understand and say "Well done",
   He'll understand and say "Well done '.

# 123. Looking unto Jesus

*Words:* M.A. Baughen
*Music:* N.L. Warren

Looking un-to Je - sus Who has gone be - fore,

Now enthroned in glo - ry, King for ev-er-more.

Born a-gain of His Spir - it, Saved by His shed blood,

Giv - en work to be done for Him, Joined to Him by love: Looking un-to

Je - sus Who has gone be - fore, Now enthroned in

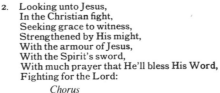

2. Looking unto Jesus,
   In the Christian fight,
   Seeking grace to witness,
   Strengthened by His might,
   With the armour of Jesus,
   With the Spirit's sword,
   With much prayer that He'll bless His Word,
   Fighting for the Lord:
   
   *Chorus*

3. Looking unto Jesus
   Who despised the shame,
   Throwing off all hindrance
   As we bear His Name.
   Help us face all temptation,
   Lord, help us discern,
   Give us courage to speak for Thee
   Help our light to burn:
   
   *Chorus*

# 124. O Jesus, Lord and Saviour

*Words:* T.O. Chisholm
*Music.* C. Lowden

O Je-sus, Lord and Saviour, I give my-self to Thee; For Thou, in Thy a-

C7  F  C7  F  Gm  D7  Gm  C7

-tonement Didst give Thy-self for me; I own no oth-er master, My heart shall

F  G7  C  F  C7  F  F7

be Thy throne; My life I give, hence-forth to live, O Christ, for Thee a-lone.

Bb  Bbm6  F  D7  G7  C7  F

# 125. I have decided

*Words:* Anon
*Music: arr.* C. Simmonds

1. I have de-ci-ded to fol-low Je-sus I have de-

D  A  D  D7

-ci-ded to follow Je-sus, I have de-ci-ded to follow

Je-sus, No turn-ing back, no turn-ing back.

2. The cross before me, the world behind me,
   The cross before me, the world behind me,
   The cross before me, the world behind me,
   No turning back, no turning back.

© C. Simmonds 1964 By kind permission

# 126. Lord Jesus Christ

*Words and Music:* P. Appleford

1. Lord Je-sus Christ, You have come to us,

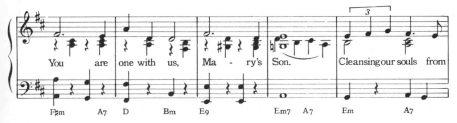

You are one with us, Ma-ry's Son. Cleansing our souls from

all their sin Pouring your love and good-ness in, Je-sus, our love for

you we sing,   Liv - ing Lord.        Lord.

D    B7    Em7    A7    D        Dm7    A7        D

*At*          2. Lord Jesus Christ,
*Communion*      Now and every day,
                 Teach us how to pray,
                     Son of God.
                 You have commanded us to do
                 This in remembrance, Lord, of You:
                 Into our lives Your power breaks through,
                     Living Lord.

             3. Lord Jesus Christ,
                You have come to us,
                Born as one of us,
                    Mary's Son.
                Led out to die on Calvary,
                Risen from death to set us free,
                Living Lord Jesus, help us see
                    You are Lord.

             4. Lord Jesus Christ,
                I would come to You,
                Live my life for You,
                    Son of God.
                All Your commands I know are true,
                Your many gifts will make me new,
                Into my life Your power breaks through,
                    Living Lord.

# The Mission of the Church

## 127. Reigning Lord

*Words:* J.E. Seddon
*Music:* P. Appleford (as No. 126)

*(To be sung to the tune of No. 126)*

1.  To Him we come:
    Jesus Christ our Lord,
    God's own living Word,
    His dear Son.
    In Him there is no east and west,
    In Him all nations shall be blest,
    To all He offers peace and rest,
    Loving Lord.

2.  In Him we live:
    Christ our strength and stay,
    Life, and Truth, and Way,
    Friend divine.
    His power can break the chains of sin,
    Still all life's storms without, within,
    Help us the daily fight to win,
    Living Lord.

3.  For Him we go
    Soldiers of the cross,
    Counting all things loss,
    Him to know;
    Going to men of every race,
    Preaching to all His wondrous grace,
    Building His Church in every place,
    Conquering Lord.

4.  With Him we serve:
    His the work we share
    With saints everywhere,
    Near and far;
    One in the task which faith requires,
    One in the zeal which never tires,
    One in the hope His love inspires,
    Coming Lord.

5.  Onward we go,
    Faithful, bold, and true,
    His blest will to do,
    Day by day.
    Till, at the last, with joy, we'll see
    Jesus, in glorious majesty;
    Live with Him through eternity,
    Reigning Lord!

# 128. Every person in every nation

*Words and Music:* Wycliffe Bible Translators

**Deliberately (not too fast)**

Ev - 'ry per - son in ev - 'ry nat - ion In each succeed - ing gen - er - a - tion

Db  Ebm7  Db  Db7  Ebm  Bb  Ebm  Ab  Db  Ab7  Db  Db7  Ebm  Bb  Ebm  Ab7

Has the right to hear the news That Christ can save. Cru - ci - fied on

Db  Gb  Db  Eb9  Eb7  Ab  Ab7  Db  Ebm7  Db  Db7

Cal - v'ry's mountain He op-ened wide a cleansing foun-tain Con - quered sin and

Bbm  Bb  Ebm  Ab  Db  Ab7  Db  Db7  Ebm  Bb7  Ebm  Ab  Db  Gbm

**Slower**

death and hell, He rose up from the grave. Fa - ther, I am will - ing To

Db  Dbm  Eb7  Ab7  Db  A  Em  A7  Db

ded - i - cate to Thee Life and ta-lent, time and mon-ey: Here am I send me.

Ab  Ab+  Db  Gb  Db  Bbm6  F  Bbm  Eb7  Ab7  Db

# 129. A vessel called the Church of God

*Words and Music:* M.G. Schneider
*tr.* S. Lonsdale and adapted by M.A. Baughen

A vessel called the Church of God Sails ov - er time's great sea; She sets her course for God's great port To God's e - ter - ni - ty. The world at - tacks her like a storm, There's dan - ger need, and fear; She

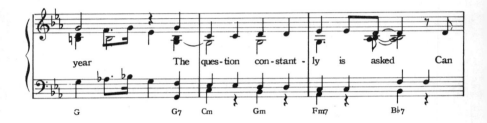

sails with hope and vic - tor - y Through ev - 'ry pass - ing

Cm6    D9    Gm    Cm    Cm6    D7

year    The ques - tion con - stant - ly is asked Can

G    G7    Cm    Gm    Fm7    Bb7

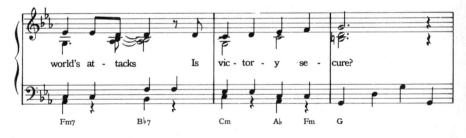

this great ship en - dure?    Can she sur - vive the

Cm    Bb7    Cm    G    G7    Cm    Gm

world's at - tacks    Is vic - tor - y se - cure?

Fm7    Bb7    Cm    Ab    Fm    G

CHORUS

We can tri - umph, Lord, As You stay with us, Lord, We will

Ab    Eb    Ab    Eb    G7

sail on the tur - bu - lent sea of this life And sail with You as Lord!

Cm      B♭7      Cm      G7(♭9)      Cm      Fm7   G7      Cm

2. What happens if the ship remains
At moorings by the quay?
What happens if she wants the calm
And will not put to sea?
    It may be nice to glory in
    The vict'ries of the past,
    But God wants us to sail today—
    His colours at the mast!
The course of God is sacrifice,
We must not fear the cost;
The life not lived for Christ the Lord
Is life which God calls lost:
    *Chorus*

3. The ship we call the Church of God
Depends upon its crew;
There are no passengers aboard,
There's work for all to do.
    God has a post for ev'ryone,
    A duty to fulfil;
    He gifted us, now looks to us,
    To do His perfect will.
We work together as a team
With fellowship in Him,
We have a common faith and hope—
The Spirit's power within:
    *Chorus*

4. The ship has many would-be guides
Who state what course they think;
They rest upon man's thought alone
And with them we would sink!
    But God has made His course quite clear,
    His way is in His Word;
    We see the fulness of the truth
    As we look to the Lord.
When onslaughts come upon our faith
Let courage flood our hearts;
We are a world-wide fellowship
And share all God imparts:
    *Chorus*

# 130. There's a road

*Words and Music:* M.G. Schneider
*tr.* S. Lonsdale and adapted by M.A. Baughen

1. There's a road which leads from Je-ru-sa-lem, It's the way down to Je-ri-cho, It's Com-passion road, steep and tir-ing road, Which has dan-ger from thiev-ing foe. And here on this road is one man Beaten

up and left as half dead, Like many in this world a-round us Op-
-pressed, in des-pair or un-fed. Hear him cry out As he
lies on Compas-sion road.

2. Watch a priest and levite come down that road
   Only giving the man small heed,
   They are too caught up with religious thoughts
   To give help to a man in need.
   Samaritan, walk behind them!
   You are not within the same class!
   But you are the one who helps him—
   You could not see need and just pass!
   You heard the cry
   As you walked on Compassion road.

3. The Compassion road goes right on through life,
   It's a road with us still today,
   Many hands are needed to give the help
   To those stricken upon the way.
   So now will you have compassion?
   To the lonely, hungry, and worn,
   To those without hope or salvation
   To fearful and poor and forlorn?
   Lord, give us grace
   To give help on Compassion road.

# 131. The fields are white

*Words and Music:* M.A. Baughen

**Calypso rhythm**

The | fields are white un-to | har-vest time, Look | up and see! | The

G — D₇

CHORUS

fields are white un-to | har-vest time, Look | up and see: | Pray to the

G₇ — C — D₇ — G

Lord of the har-vest, | Christ says pray. | Pray to the | Lord for the workers

Am — D₇ — G — D₇ — G₇ — C — Am A₇

*for repeat*

Which we need in this | day. | | *last time only* day.

D₇ — G — D₇ — G

2. The harvest truly is fit to reap
But workers few,
The harvest truly is fit to reap
But workers few:
*Chorus*

3. Who else will 'go into all the world'
To preach the Word?
Who else will 'go into all the world'
To preach the Word?
*Chorus*

4. The Lord's return may be very soon,
The time is short!
The Lord's return may be very soon,
The time is short:
*Chorus*

# 132. Go forth and tell

*Words:* J.E. Seddon
*Music:* M.A. Baughen

**With a swing**

1. Go forth and tell! O Church of God, a - wake! God's sav-ing news to all the na-tions take. Pro - claim Christ Je - sus, Sav-iour Lord, and King, That all the world His worthy praise may sing.

2. Go forth and tell! God's love embraces all:
He will in grace respond to all who call.
How shall they call if they have never heard
The gracious invitation of His Word?

3. Go forth and tell! Men still in darkness lie:
In wealth or want, in sin they live and die.
Give us, O Lord, concern of heart and mind,
A love like Thine which cares for all mankind.

4. Go forth and tell! The doors are open wide:
Share God's good gifts with men so long denied.
Live out your life as Christ, your Lord, shall choose,
Your ransomed powers for His sole glory use.

5. Go forth and tell! O Church of God, arise:
Go in the strength which Christ your Lord supplies.
Go, till all nations His great Name adore
And serve Him Lord and King for evermore.

# The Heavenly Hope

## 133. O when the saints go marching in

Traditional *arr.* D.G. Wilson

O when the | saints _____ go marching | in, _____ O when the
(O when the saints) | (go march-ing in)

saints go march-ing | in; _____ O Lord, I | want to be a-mong the

Gm    C7    F    F7

num-ber _____ When the | saints go march-ing | in. _____

Bb    Gm    Am7 Bbmaj7 F6    C9    F

2. O when they crown Him Lord of all,
O when they crown Him Lord of all;
O Lord, I want to be among the number
When they crown Him Lord of all.

3. O when all knees bow at His name,
O when all knees bow at His name;
O Lord, I want to be among the number
When all knees bow at His name.

4. O when they sing the Saviour's praise,
O when they sing the Saviour's praise;
O Lord, I want to be among the number
When they sing the Saviour's praise.

5. O when the saints go marching in,
O when the saints go marching in;
O Lord, I want to be among the number
When the saints go marching in.

# 134. I gotta home

Traditional *arr.* M.C.T. Strover

1. I got-ta home in glo - ry - land that out-shines the sun,

I got-ta home in glo - ry - land that out-shines the sun,

I got-ta home in glo - ry - land that out - shines the sun,

Way be-yond the blue:

CHORUS

Do Lord, oh, do Lord, oh, do re-mem-ber me;

Do Lord, oh, do Lord, oh, do remem-ber me;

Do Lord, oh, do Lord, oh, do re-mem-ber me;

G6    B7    Em7    A7

Way be - yond the blue.

G6    D9    G6    (C#♭9    Gmaj7)

The verse accompaniment may be used for the chorus if the latter is found too hard.

2.  I took Jesus as my Saviour,
    you take Him too . . . .

3.  If you will not bear a cross,
    you can't wear a crown . . .

*Alternative version*

1.  I gotta home in gloryland
        that outshines the sun,
    I gotta home in gloryland
        that outshines the sun,
    I gotta home in gloryland
        that outshines the sun,
    Way beyond the blue:

*Chorus*  Thank You, my Saviour, for that eternal life;
    Thank You, my Saviour, for that eternal life;
    Thank You, my Saviour, for that eternal life
    With You evermore!

2.  Those who trust in Christ as Saviour
        shall never die. . .

3.  If you will not bear a cross,
        you can't wear a crown. . .

# 135. When I come

*Words:* T. Ramsey
*Music:* C.E. Durham

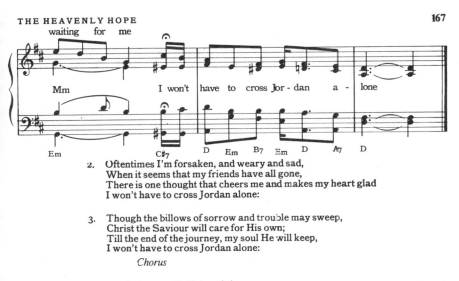

Mm    I won't have to cross Jor-dan a-lone

2. Oftentimes I'm forsaken, and weary and sad,
   When it seems that my friends have all gone,
   There is one thought that cheers me and makes my heart glad
   I won't have to cross Jordan alone:

3. Though the billows of sorrow and trouble may sweep,
   Christ the Saviour will care for His own;
   Till the end of the journey, my soul He will keep,
   I won't have to cross Jordan alone:
   
   *Chorus*

## 136. This world is not my home

Traditional *arr*. G.R. Timms

1. This world is not my home, I'm just a-pass-ing through; My
treasures are laid up Some-where be-yond the blue; The Sav-iour beckons me From
hea-ven's op-en door, And I can't feel at home In this world an-y more.

O Lord, you know, I have no friend like you, If
hea-ven's not my home Then, Lord what will I do? The Saviour beckons me From
hea-ven's op-en door, And I can't feel at home in this world an-y more.

2. They're all expecting me,
   And that's one thing I know,
   My Saviour pardoned me,
   Now onward I must go;
   I know He'll take me through
   Though I am weak and poor,
   And I can't feel at home
   In this world any more.
   *Chorus*

3. Just over in glory land
   We'll live eternally,
   The saints on every hand
   Are shouting victory;
   Their songs of sweetest praise
   Drift back from heaven's shore,
   And I can't feel at home
   In this world any more.
   *Chorus*

# Spirituals

## 137. O sinner man

Traditional
*arr.* (piano) D.G. Wilson

O sin-ner man, where will you run to? O sin-ner man, where will you run to?
O sin-ner man, where will you run to, All on that day?

**Start with chorus**

1. Run to the rocks, rocks won't you hide me?
   Run to the rocks, rocks won't you hide me?
   Run to the rocks, rocks won't you hide me,
   All on that day?

   *Chorus*

2. Run to the sea, sea is a-boiling,
   Run to the sea, sea is a-boiling,
   Run to the sea, sea is a-boiling,
   All on that day?

   *Chorus*

3. Run to the Lord, Lord won't you hide me?
   Run to the Lord, Lord won't you hide me?
   Run to the Lord, Lord won't you hide me,
   All on that day?

   *Chorus*

4. O sinner man, should bin a-praying.
   O sinner man, should bin a-praying,
   O sinner man, should bin a-praying,
   All on that day?

   *Chorus*

## 137. O sinner man

Traditional
*arr.* (vocal) M.C.T. Strover

**CHORUS**

O sin-ner man, where will you run to? O sin-ner man, where will you run to?
(Hum) Mm   Mm   Mm   Mm

O sin-ner man, where will you run to, All on that day?

Mm Mm Mm Mm Mm

Em D Em

**VERSE 1.**

Run to the rocks, Rocks won't you hide me? Run to the rocks, Rocks won't you hide me?

Rrrun Rrrun Rrrun Rrrun *simile.*

Em D

Run to the rocks, Rocks won't you hide me? All on that day:

Em D Em

**VERSE 2.**

Run to the sea, sea is a-boil-ing, Run to the sea, sea is a-boil-ing,

Run to the sea, sea is a-boil-ing, Run to the sea, sea is a-boil-

Run to the sea, sea is a-boil-ing, Run to the sea, sea is a-

Run to the sea, sea is a-boil-ing, Run to the sea, sea

*End with chorus*

# 138. If religion were a thing

Traditional (African)
*arr.* C. Simmonds

2.  Christ died for us all, He died upon the tree,
    But now He lives, He lives in me:
    
    *Chorus*

3.  We praise Thee, O God, we acknowledge Thee
    To be the Lord, the Lord most high:
    
    *Chorus*

*Alternative version*

1.  Our Father which art in heaven
    Hallowed be Thy Name; Thy kingdom come,
    
    *Chorus*

2.  Thy will be done in earth as in heaven
    Put us not to the test, lead us not into wrong.
    
    *Chorus*

# 139. You've got to walk that lonesome valley

Traditional *arr.* G. R. Timms

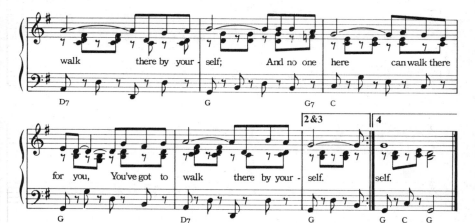

2.  You've got to face one day your Maker,
    You've got to face Him by yourself;
    And no one here can face Him for you,
    You've got to face Him by yourself.

3.  You've got to stand one day in Judgement,
    You've got to stand there by yourself;
    And no one here can stand there for you,
    You've got to stand there by yourself.

4.  You've got to walk that lonesome valley,
    You've got to walk there by yourself;
    And no one here can walk there for you,
    You've got to walk there by yourself.

© Copyright in this arrangement by G.R. Timms 1964 By kind permission

# 140. Were you there when they crucified my Lord?

Traditional *arr.* P.C. Butler

2. Were you there when they nailed Him to the tree?..

3. Were you there when they pierced Him in the side?..

4. Were you there when the sun refused to shine?..

5. Were you there when they laid Him in the tomb?..

6. Were you there when He rose up from the dead?
   Were you there when He rose up from the dead?
   O-o-oh! Sometimes I feel like shouting glory,
         glory, glory.
   Were you there when He rose up from the dead?

# 141. Steal away

Traditional *arr.* M.C.T. Strover

2. Green trees are bending,
   The sinner stands a-trembling;
   The trumpet sounds within my soul;
   I ain't got long to stay here:

   *Chorus*

3. My Lord He calls me;
   He calls me by the lightning
   The trumpet sounds within my soul;
   I ain't got long to stay here:

   *Chorus*

# 142. Do you love my Lord?

Traditional *arr.* G. R. Timms

2. Makes us feel like shouting when you love my Jesus;
Makes us feel like shouting when you love my Lord:
I want to know, yes, I want to know,
Do you love my Lord?
*Chorus*

3. Shout it from the mountains if you love my Jesus;
Sing it in the valleys if you love my Lord:
I want to know, yes, I want to know,
Do you love my Lord?
*Chorus*

# 143. Little David

Traditional *arr.* M.C.T. Strover

**N.B.** Some sing as the chorus: Little David followed the Lord,
Why don't you? Why don't you?

*Start with chorus*

*Chorus*   Little David, play on your harp,
Hallelu, Hallelu,
Little David play on your harp,
Hallelu.

1. Little David was a shepherd boy;
He killed Goliath, shouted for joy:
*Chorus*

2. Joshua was the son of Nun,
He never would quit till the work was done:
*Chorus*

# 144. The gospel train

Traditional *arr.* M.C.T. Strover

When possible, this should be performed with two guitars, one taking the bass
figure, the other the harmony of the voice part, and 'engine whistle' chords.

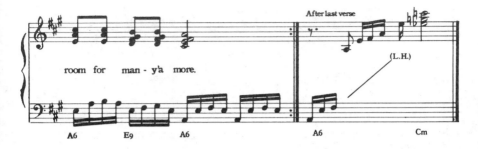

room for man-y'a more.

(L.H.)

A6    E9    A6              A6              Cm

2. I hear the bell and whistle, a-coming round the curve,
   She's playing all the steam and power, and straining every nerve:
   *Chorus*

3. The fare is cheap and all can go, the rich and poor are there,
   No second class aboard that train, no difference in the fare:
   *Chorus*

4. No signal for another train to follow on the line,
   O sinner, you're for ever lost if once you're left behind:
   *Chorus*

5. She's nearing now the station— O sinner, don't be vain;
   O come and get your ticket, and be ready for that train:
   *Chorus*

# 145. Lord I want to be a Christian in my heart

Traditional *arr.* G. R. Timms

Lord, I want to be a Christian in my

D    G6    A9    D    G    D         D         G6    A7

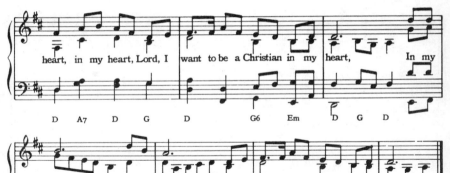

heart, in my heart, Lord, I want to be a Christian in my heart, In my

heart, in my heart, Lord, I want to be a Christian in my heart.

1.  Lord, I want to be a Christian in my heart, in my heart,
    Lord, I want to be a Christian in my heart,
    In my heart, in my heart,
    Lord, I want to be a Christian in my heart.

2.  Lord, I want to be more loving in my heart...

3.  Lord, I want to be more holy in my heart...

4.  Lord, I want to be like Jesus in my heart...

# 146. Joshua fought the battle of Jericho

Traditional *arr.* M.C.T. Strover

Josh - ua fought the bat - tle of Je - ri - cho,

Je - ri - cho, Je - ri - cho, Josh - ua fought the battle of Je - ri - cho, And the

walls came a-tumbling down.

1. You may talk of your King of Gib-e-on, You may talk of your man of Saul, There's none like good old Jos-hu-a, And the battle of Je-ri-cho:

2. Up to the walls of Je-ri-cho He marched with spear in hand, "Go blow them rams horns" Joshua cried, "For the battle is in my hand."

3. Then the lam rams sheephorns be-gin to blow, Trumpets be-gan to sound; Joshua commanded the peo-ple to shout, And the walls came a-tum-bl-ing down:

# 147. Goin' to lay down my burden

Traditional *arr.* G. R. Timms

CHORUS

Ain't goin' to grieve my Lord no more, Ain't goin' to grieve my Lord no

G    D  Dm6    Am         D                      G         G7

more,    Ain't goin' to    grieve    my    Lord    no    more;

C                  Am              G    D    G

Ain't goin' to grieve my Lord no more, Ain't goin' to grieve my Lord no

D  Dm6    Am         D              G         G7

more, Ain't goin' to    grieve    my    Lord    no    more.

C          Am    Bm    Am D   G   Bm Am  G

2. Goin' to lay down my sword and shield...

3. Goin' to try on my long white robe...

4. Goin' to try on my starry crown...

*Alternative version*

1. Goin' to lay down my burden...

2. Goin' to sing for my Saviour...

3. Goin' to talk to my Maker...

4. Goin' to follow my Master...

# 148. Somebody's knocking at your door

Traditional *arr.* M.C.T. Strover

VERSE 1.

Some - bo - dy's knocking at your door, Somebo - dy's knocking at your door; O sin - ner, why don't you ans - wer? Somebo - dy's knocking at your door. *Fine.*

VERSES 2, 3 & 4

2. Knocks like Je - sus, Some - bo - dy's knocking at your door;

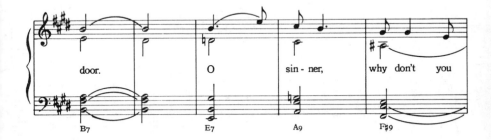

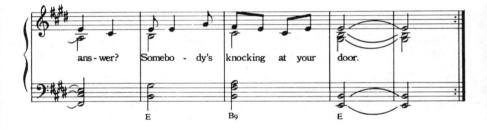

3. Can't you hear Him?
Somebody's knocking at your door;
Can't you hear Him?
Somebody's knocking at your door.
O sinner, why don't you answer?
Somebody's knocking at your door.

4. Answer Jesus,
Somebody's knocking at your door;
Answer Jesus,
Somebody's knocking at your door.
O sinner, why don't you answer?
Somebody's knocking at your door.

# 149. There is a balm in Gilead

Traditional *arr.* P.C. Butler

Start with chorus

**Chorus**  There is a balm in Gilead
To make the wounded whole,
There is a balm in Gilead
To heal the sin-sick soul.

1. Sometimes I feel discouraged
   And think my work's in vain,
   But then the Holy Spirit
   Revives my soul again:
   *Chorus*

2. You cannot sing like angels,
   You cannot preach like Paul,
   But you can tell of Jesus
   And say He died for all:
   *Chorus*

# 150. Go tell it on the mountain

Traditional *arr.* ...

**2.** He made me a watchman,
Upon the city wall;
To tell of His salvation,
For Jesus died for all:
*Chorus*

**3.** Go tell it to your neighbour
In darkness here below;
Go with the words of Jesus,
That all the world may know:
*Chorus*

# INDEX OF TITLES AND FIRST LINES

*The first line of a piece is included, in italic type, only where it differs from the title.*

## More Falcons

### Taught by pain

*Mary Endersbee (editor)*

Valerie Hadert (author of No. 279 in this book), Jack Wallace, Barbara Piller (formerly Mrs John Clayton), and the editor tell their own stories, showing how they have learned from God through suffering. **30p**

### He is everything to me

*Ian Barclay*

This author's second book is in a similar style to his already popular *Facts of the Matter* (see opposite page) but on a very different subject. Here is a modern devotional book on Psalm 23 all will find helpful. **30p**

### God at ground level

*Ralph Capenerhurst and Eddy Stride*

In this very human, and often humorous, account of life in a large railway works, Ralph Capenerhurst highlights some of the problems of Christian witness in an industrial setting. Eddy Stride has written a brief commentary on each chapter. **30p**

### Who was this man?

*Gavin Reid*

A very simple introduction to what we believe about the Lord Jesus Christ: who He was and why He is important. **7½p**

### What can I do?

*Gavin Reid*

A simple, thoughtful, practical booklet, on the important subject of vocation. **10p**

# More Falcons

### Journey into life

*Norman Warren*

A basic guide to becoming a Christian, written in a very straightforward style, with frequent helpful pictures and diagrams. Half a million copies sold.                                                                 **5p**

### The Case against Christ

*John Young*

A crisp, easy-to-read clash with popular objections to the Christian faith; faces the challenge of science, the fact of other religions, the trustworthiness of the Bible, and whether God's existence can be proved.     **25p**

### The Facts of the Matter

*Ian Barclay*

A presentation of some basic Christian beliefs in the readable style of one of today's popular preachers.                                           **25p**

### My God is real

*David C. K. Watson*

This readable book sets out the basics of the Christian gospel as understood by one of Britain's outstanding young preachers.                      **30p**

### Beginning a new life with Christ

*John Stott*

An evangelistic booklet (the substance of six broadcast talks on Jesus Christ).                                                                  **5p**

For a complete list of the range of Falcon books and booklets write to:

**CPAS PUBLICATIONS**
**Falcon Court, 32 Fleet Street, London EC4Y 1DB**

# Filmstrips from CPAS

### Pilgrim's Progress
Set of six filmstrips
*Artwork by Gordon Stowell*

A modern interpretation of John Bunyan's book. The timeless and universal truths of the story are presented in a way which frees them from the trappings of time and place.

### World of work
Single filmstrip
*Artwork by Robert Hewerdine*

This filmstrip is based on a chapter in the Falcon book *On the Job*, and is intended as an introduction to 'the world of work' for young Christians going into industry, although it will be useful, too, to those who have been at work some time.

### Authority of Scripture
Single filmstrip
*Artwork by Richard Knight*

This filmstrip shows *why* we should seek Christ in the Scriptures – the reasons for believing in its supreme authority and what results follow from accepting this authority.

### John Newton
Single filmstrip
*Artwork by Anthony Baurepaire*

'The old African blasphemer' he called himself; slave trader turned preacher and hymn-writer, John Newton was a marvel to many. This is the story of the transformation of a life whose effects are still felt today.

For a complete list of CPAS audio-visual aids write to:
**CPAS PUBLICATIONS**
**Falcon Court, 32 Fleet Street, London EC4Y 1DB**